Constructive Beekeeping

Written and illustrated
by
Norman John Chapman

published by

CMI Publishing Ltd

Written and illustrated by Norman John Chapman

Edited by Valerie Rhenius, B Sc

Printed by Colourflow Ltd,
Farnborough, Surrey, UK

ISBN 0-9541700-0-8

Published by
CMI Publishing Ltd,
Baythorne Cottage, Baythorne End,
Halstead, Essex, CO9 4AB, UK

http://www.constructive-beekeeping.co.uk
http://www.cmipublishing.co.uk

Chapters

Acknowledgements

This book has been several years in preparation. My thanks are due to everyone who gave tips and passed on their own findings, everyone who helped with holding various gadgets for my photos (in preparation for the illustrations), and to the many specialists in several fields who have during this time, given their help with interest and alacrity. They include:

Ken Audsley (deceased), a Surrey Beekeeper, for wiring

Joan Chapman, my wife, for putting up with it for so long, bees and all

Malcolm Clarke, a prominent Surrey Beekeeper, for checking the manuscript

Dave Dawson, Canada, for the tip on clearing supers and minimising backache (chapter 3.2)

A V Dodge, a senior member of the Quekett Microscopical Club, for a mine of microscopy information

Elizabeth Duffin for help with wax

Andrew Gibb, a Director of 'Beecraft', for beekeeping advice

Fred Howard, a Surrey Beekeeper, for information on foundation, and for holding the smoker for the photo on the front cover

James Morton, B Sc, Regional Bee Inspector, for advice on bee health

Brian Reynolds, Poth & Hille, for much wax information

Valerie Rhenius, my daughter, for editing the book

Karl Showler, B & K Books, for foundation history

Richard Stimson, a Surrey Beekeeper, for much wax information

and a great many others, far outnumbering those mentioned above, most of whom I have never met, but who have taken the trouble to write about their findings, and hence have had an influence on the writing of this book.

The Author

Norman Chapman is a retired electronics engineer. He has kept bees in Surrey, UK for over twenty years. He has been an active member of Wimbledon Beekeepers, and has taken a prominent role in presenting beekeeping at local, county and national shows, notably the managing of a DIY stand for several years at the annual National Honey Show held in London each autumn.

An inveterate experimenter, he has devised and unearthed several advantageous ways and means to make beekeeping easier for beekeepers from the many promising blind alleys that he has investigated.

Suppliers, Sources and Trademarks

2.6   Alec Tiranti Ltd., 70 High Street, Theale, Reading, Berkshire, RG7 5AR, UK.

2.8   Tel: 0118 930 2775   Also at 27 Warren Street, London, W1P 5DG.
         Tel: 020 7636 8565   Web address: http://www.tiranti.co.uk
         E-mail: enquiries@tiranti.co.uk

2.6   W.P.Notcutt Ltd, 25 Church Road, Teddington, Middlesex, TW11 8PF.
         Tel: 020 8977 2252 Web address: http://www.notcutt.co.uk
         E-mail: sales@notcutt.co.uk

2.8   The Fibreglass Shop, 197 High Street, Brentford, Middlesex, TW8 8AH.
         Tel: 020 8568 1645

2.8   Locker Wire Weavers Ltd, Farrell Street, Warrington, Cheshire, WA1 2WW.
         Tel: 01925 651212 Web address: http://www.lockerwire.co.uk
         E-mail: sales@lockerwire.co.uk

3.9   National Bee Unit, Central Science Laboratory, Sand Hutton, York, YO41 1LZ,
         UK.   Tel: 01904 462000 E-mail: science@csl.gov.uk
            Web address: http://www.csl.gov.uk/prodserv/cons/bee/

5.0   Poth Hille & Co Ltd, High Street, Stratford, London, E15 2QD.
         Tel: 020 8534 7091   Web address: http://www.poth-hille.co.uk

5.0   The British Wax Refining Co Ltd, 62 Holmthorpe Avenue, Holmthorpe
         Industrial Estate, Redhill, Surrey, RH1 2NL, UK. Tel: 01737 761242

Apistan® Anti-Varroa Mite Strip is a registered trademark of Wellmark International.
Araldite® is the trademark of Ciba Geigy Ltd
Bayvarol® is a registered trade mark of Bayer plc.
CAB-O-SIL® is a registered trademark of Cabot Corp
Melinex® is a registered trademark of DuPont Teijin Films
Plastilene, Plasticene, Plasteline or Plastelina are all variations of the name describing a
         wax based clay, registered by, and still manufactured by Chavant Inc
Pozidriv® is a registered trademark of the Phillips Screw Company
Sellotape® is a registered trademark of Sellotape GB Limited
Workmate® is a registered trademark of Black & Decker in the U.K.

Information on other organisations and publications etc is given on the links page of our website.
If you wish to be included, please e-mail us: constructive-beekeeping@dial.pipex.com
Web address: http://www.constructive-beekeeping.co.uk

Constructive Beekeeping

Health & Safety

Safe Working Practice

You are advised to take precautions to minimise any risks involved in using electrical equipment, tools, hot substances and solvents. Courses, which you would be well advised to follow, are available for learning to use hazardous equipment safely.

For general workshop safety, always keep handy a fire extinguisher suitable for electrical fires, and have electric shock and resuscitation charts clearly displayed near the benches. It is recommended not to work totally alone: someone should be within sight and/or sound to render help and raise the alarm in case of accident.

Wear safety goggles where there is any danger to the eyes, eg from sparks, or spitting of hot wax or solvents.

Safety Legislation

COSHH (Control of Substances Hazardous to Health Act) is concerned with minimising the risks to health of substances used in the workshop: solders, fluxes, solvents, detergents, aerosols, inflammable materials etc.

Make sure you (and anyone you are responsible for) are aware of the nature of the substances you are using and the safe way of using them. Familiarise yourself with and follow manufacturers' and suppliers' instructions carefully. Hand in hand with this goes the provision of safe storage areas and the means of safe dispensing; attention to ventilation and the provision of protective clothing, gloves and face masks where applicable.

Health and safety data sheets are available from manufacturers and suppliers of service aids and materials, and a wall poster 'Hazardous Substances on these Premises', is widely available. Further information is available from the Health and Safety Executive (HSE), and they are listed in local telephone directories.

Introduction

Commendable leading beekeepers have taken to the pen and left us valuable books, standard handbooks, describing bee biology, manipulations, handling hive products, season's work, beehive design, bee troubles, etc. These overall text and reference works have to cover so much important ground that much of the details of how to go about the many routines that are supportive just have to be left out, simply that time and space have to call a limit.

This work is complementary. It concentrates on those back-up processes, and includes many items not previously published, and subjects insufficiently detailed or aired in other literature. It enables a beekeeper, not long started, to get into it quickly, with a newly prompted awareness of relevant problems; a guide through a perennial trail of stumbling blocks.

This is a collection of essential processes, conveniences and knowhows that I have learnt over the years. Some have been published by others. A few, I have devised. Some wiser ones say things like 'Any fool could have worked that out', but there are so many knacks to support the practice that no one can be expected to work out every trick pronto.

This book will save you months of frustration. All these methods and preparations otherwise take several years to accumulate suitable familiarity, too often by expensive and time consuming trial and error. I have picked out those subjects and items most likely to be useful to the small scale beekeeper, the beginner and those with a memory like mine.

I've often hankered to collect together all the impressive constructive and fulfilling articles from the magazines to make a manual of this kind, but the overwhelming editing job involved would have been quite impossible for a magazine to compile, for all the beekeeping ones are already run on a shoestring or are unpaid labours of love.

This book is unfinished. It never will be finished. The tricks up one's sleeve for getting the most out of ones efforts are virtually endless. All the ways, means and creations that I have described are based upon my own manipulations and observations.

It is the sort of book I would have liked to have had around when I started up. Many missing links were unfilled, and I was left to stumble, or otherwise sort them out as best as I could. This book is the fruits of my stumblings.

Work Station

It must be realised at the outset that every aspect of DIY is eased with a suitable place to work, and this is centred on the work bench. Inspecting and progressing a job, using only the floor or back yard to support it is acceptable only as a very temporary expedient. The effectiveness and accuracy of all the hand tools and most of the power tools is significantly improved, once you have a stable work bench, and at the right height.

A portable bench such as a Workmate® (fig 1.1A), or a home-made alternative, does have the merit of enabling one to work without stooping, kneeling or sitting on the floor, but these really come into their own because of their ready portability and stowage. They can be taken to help a job to be carried out upstairs or in the garden, or even taken to another site. Don't be over-enthusiastic though. Sometimes greater stability is needed for a particular job in hand. When sawing, or planing timber for example, one shouldn't need to hold the bench down with one foot. A work bench fixed to the wall (see fig 1.1B) or to the floor is the best way to start. It is the basic facility for all seasoned constructors. Sawing, drilling and filing, so often entail pushing hard to get the cutting action, thus the work often needs clamping down. Furthermore, unless the bench itself is fixed down firmly there isn't much to be gained by clamping the workpiece to it.

A successful bench can be constructed even where there is little space. A stout bench top can be hinged by one edge to a wall, of, say, a garage, so that it can be swung up out of the way when not in use. The opposite edge bears a leg frame, itself upon hinges, which swings into place when the bench is set down. When out of use the bench can be clipped up against the wall, clear of the floor; clear of the central area, and in eg the gatage, the car can then be driven into its overnight place. This arrangement has served me well for quite a few years. It does have at least one downright advantage in that each session starts with a clear top surface.

If any dimension is of concern it will be the height of the working surface from the floor. This height will exceed that of a desk or dining table which is almost standard at 28.5 inches (72cm). A small fixed bench in my garage is 39 inches (99cm) high. My foldaway bench is only 32 inches (81.5cm) high. So the height can vary widely. If you are fastidious you must answer the classic question: "What is the main usage of the bench?"

Fig 1.1A   Black & Decker Workmate® work bench.
The dual height Workmate. Good for portability.
Sometimes greater stability is needed (Fig 1.1B)

The last lap is completed by clamps of some kind or other. I write in the plural here because no one clamp will hold every sort of workpiece. The basic universal clamp is the bench vice. Should the available working surface be so limited that even a three inch vice often gets in the way, then I recommend a Record Imp. This model can be clamped on the edge of a bench, and deserves a mention because, when that part of the work is done it can be taken off so easily, or shifted to another part of the bench. Other clamps, the F clamp, the G clamp and toolmaker's clamps, will each perform well, especially on glueing jobs. Don't forget spring grips and bulldog clips. They all have their uses.

Some of the bigger projects, ready for glueing, which these clamps just cannot embrace, can set a poser. This type of problem can usually be remedied by weighting down. So often I've reached for jars heavy with nuts and bolts, big tins of paints and gallon (5L) tins of oil in order to apply pressure to the necessary joints. I've even used elastic luggage hooks for holding glued joints tightly together.

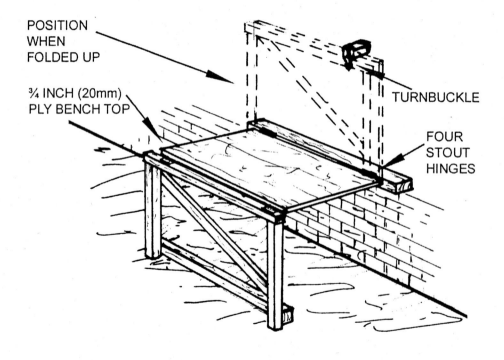

POSITION WHEN FOLDED UP

¾ INCH (20mm) PLY BENCH TOP

TURNBUCKLE

FOUR STOUT HINGES

Fig 1.1B   Fold up work bench.

Materials and Resources

The following sections dealing with wood, metals and other materials, are included because a knowledge of and familiarity with these can be so useful. An interest in the properties, under stresses of temperature and moisture etc., give a significant advantage in constructional and repair tasks when assessing the worth of recyclable materials that are obtainable easily, often just for the asking.

The usefulness of such an interest in what can be expected of raw materials goes much further than just wood, plastics and metals. Vast quantities of commonplace items in widespread production and distribution are used once and discarded. Plastic shopping bags, paper clips, cardboard boxes, packing materials, textiles, wire, tubing and plasterboard; an endless list. In nearly all cases, after good usage, these materials fully retain the properties for which they were initially selected, through a long, redundant languish, a brief spell in a dustbin or a skip, and into the ignominious dump.

Fig 1.2A Scrap yards where abandoned junk collections can always be found.
Endless resources of reusable material.

Fig 1.2B The magnet test. Iron screws are easily separated.
The other metals do not corrode so easily.

Furthermore, complete collections of resources are cast aside *en bloc* in the form of worn out motor cars, refrigerators, typewriters, gas fires and furniture. Each one is written off because it is no longer economic to repair.

I found that the stout clips often used to bind large cardboard boxes, those made of flat wire, are perfect for repairing the corners of wooden framed queen excluders. I found a discarded load of bonded underfelt offcuts. This perfectly suited the insulation I needed for a solar panel. I was actually looking for a 4 inch (10.2cm) diameter plastic water pipe offcut when I came across a skip containing a large quantity of it. Millions of wooden pallets are used for storage and shipment of packaged wares. Millions are discarded, largely because one part is damaged; one member is broken. One of these can still support a beehive. I've collected many, and now use nothing else. A broken house brick placed on the roof is added security against gale force winds. Battered ply, hardboard, or lino pieces laid on the ground before the entrance is effective in discouraging long grass and weeds from smothering the hive entrance.

Fig 1.2C Scavenged wooden palletts make stable supports for hives.
A broken house brick placed on the roof is added security against gale force winds

Cardboard Boxes

When you've bottled your honey, be it 30 lb or 1000 lb (10 Kg or 1 Tonne), you will be looking for cardboard boxes, not only to carry it around in, but in which to store it until it passes jar by jar, each to a customer or other consumer. Those boxes so often available freely from the supermarkets are rarely suitable, most being too tall, or not stout enough or don't cuddle the jars nice and closely.

New, one pound (~0.5 Kg) jars come in half gross boxes. Holding two or three layers of empty jars, these cardboard boxes are far from suitable for containing the jars when full of honey. This is because with the lids screwed on, the jars are taller, and you can't get the top tier in and close the box lids down. Further, the filled pots increase the weight so much that the box is too flimsy to manage the load.

It wasn't obvious to me until I was shown. These same boxes, cut down, make ideal honey carriers. I slit those corners between the upright sides down to within four inches of the base, then fold the now, longer sides in, down to a one jar height. I use a made up wooden block as a jig to encourage the creases to form regularly at the correct height. The resulting flaps I cut shorter so that the opposite pairs don't overlap. One of the offcuts comes out exactly right to fill in inside the centre of the base to give a flat continuity. These modified boxes fit the jars and are ideal for transporting and stacking.

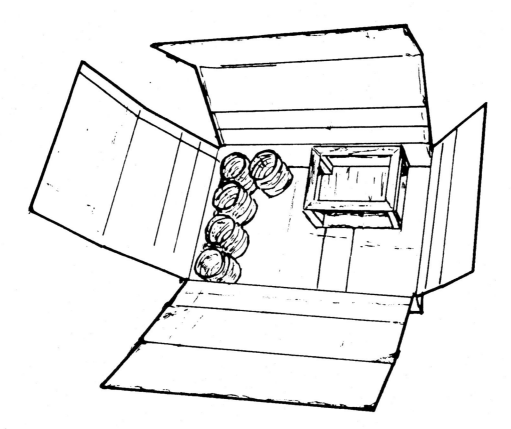

Fig 1.3   Cut down boxes, in which half gross empty jars are supplied, are far more suitable for holding filled jars. Make a bending jig from scrap timber.

Wood

The enterprising beekeeper so often finds that what he wants isn't in his supplier's catalogue. Or even if it is, it is so often quicker and cheaper to make it himself. The postage cost too, commits him to buying at beekeeping shows whenever he can.

Woods and their products are favourites for making most handy, home made assemblies. This is because they are far easier to work on than metals and perhaps more predictable than the plastics, and in general, cheaper than either, not that I buy any of them if I can avoid it. Pallets, with one part broken, are thrown out, but even like this, make ideal supports for hives. A tour round the industrial areas can reveal opportunities, and a proper request often brings surprising cooperation.

Locksmith shops often run a 24 hour shuttering service for broken windows. This entails fast boarding up with 0.75 inch (19mm) external grade plywood. Ideal for beehive boxes. "Please can I have your offcuts?" A valuable resource. When 'on the scavenge' one doesn't have to be fussy what kind of timber comes free. Although, since many beekeeping jobs are for outdoor use, then hardboard and chipboard are quite useless for this. Blockboard isn't much better.

In using salvaged timber it pays to make a point of removing all the old nails and screws, and even to cut away material in order to ensure that no nails, staples etc. are left embedded, as these can cause damage to power saws, planers, etc., and even to hand tools.

One of the problems with re-using timber is finding the space to store it. I've always got miscellaneous lengths, offcuts, plywood etc about the house and garage. This approach has paid off well time and again.

I prefer wood screws or glue, rather than nails, when fixing wooden parts together. Although this is partly fad and partly justification it is worth a mention. Iron screws are cheaper and stronger than brass ones, and last well if plated. If iron screws are to be used outdoors, make sure that they are zinc plated.

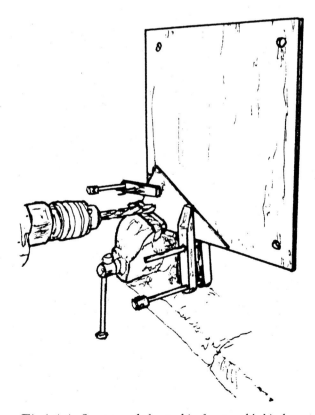

Fig 1.4A Scrap wood clamped in front and behind a work piece will leave clean edges when drilling holes

One is quite spoiled for choice when considering adhesives. When purchasing glues for woodwork one must be aware of suitability of glues in the presence of water. Some are useless. A few are styled as water resistant wood glues. These are ideal for beehives, but fail only during long term immersion. If it must be totally waterproof, use a two-part epoxy resin. The PVA water resistant adhesives however, are quite good enough and convenient for hives and general constructions. After a mistake when something is glued up the wrong way round etc., you can still get it apart. Soak the joint under water for an hour or two and then you can usually prise the two parts apart, dry them, clean them up and start again.

I often use offcut plywood to make 18.1 inch (0.46m) square (my hive plan size ie National/Commercial) boards and glue 0.75 inch (19mm) wide battens round the edges on at least one face. I have found so many handy uses that I keep several around. One can always cut the elongated holes in the central area to make them into crown cum clearer boards.

Plywood is well suited to special constructions and indeed, is in the fore of consideration for any new gadget. Be aware of two categories, internal and external. External grade is made from higher grade timbers and water resistant glue. If what you make is ever to get wet make sure that an external grade is used. If the origin of your plywood is not known, find or cut off, a small sample and immerse it overnight in water. Put a stone on it to hold it down. Internal grades start to delaminate.

When drilling blind holes to a specific depth, e.g. for wood screws, or for a plug in a wall it is difficult to judge the depth. A dab of quick drying paint placed at the required height on the drill will give a good indication. The handiest dispenser I've found is the typist's white correction fluid. An alternative is a piece of masking tape stuck round the drill.

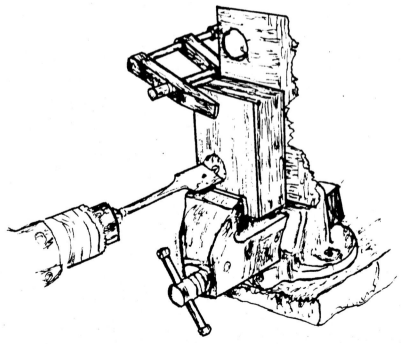

*Fig 1.4B When drilling several identical plywood pieces, clamping them together,
with a scrap piece at the back can avoid ragged edges.*

Metals

The word 'steel' means an alloy of iron, if we want to be precise. Unfortunately the expression 'mild steel' which has been bandied about the trades that deal with metals for years, is used synonymously with pure iron.

Steels fall roughly into four groups:

A.   **MILD STEEL: pure iron**
Mild steel is used for making nails, nuts and bolts, and a vast range of user products including cars, machine tools and girders.

B.   **CARBON STEEL: can be hardened and softened**
Carbon Steel contains about one percent of carbon This enables its hardness to be considerably increased by heating to a red heat and cooling quickly by plunging into water or oil. It is supplied in the soft state in which it can be drilled, cut and shaped before hardening. It can be softened again by heating to a red heat and then cooling very slowly. You can buy carbon steel rods with a ground finish in 13 inch (33cm) lengths and any diameter, imperial or metric, up to 1.5 inches (38mm) in the tool shops. It is referred to under the grandiose name of 'silver steel', but don't get excited. There's no silver in it. Files, chisels and many other hand tools are made of carbon steel. Furthermore, it is the ideal metal with which to make screwdriver blades. As an apprentice I was encouraged to make screwdrivers out of silver steel. These days, you have to be a certificated grinder for access to a grinding machine, that is, unless you own it. Courses are available and obviously you would be well advised to follow one before using one for your own health and safety.

C.   **TOOL STEEL: covers many alloys; mostly very hard, or hardenable**
Tool steels comprise iron in the main, but include selections from carbon, chromium, tungsten, nickel, manganese and silicon, etc.. These are usually encountered in the forms of high speed drills, taps, dies, ball bearings, machine parts and cutting tools, can rarely be softened by heat treatment, and can only be shaped at home by grinding.

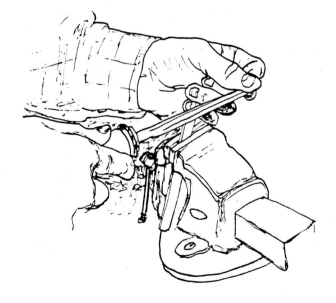

D.   **STAINLESS STEEL: an alloy; includes chromium; resists rust**
Stainless steel describes a range of alloys, but always includes a proportion of chromium. Usually fails the magnet test.

Fig 1.5A A test for hardness. Can it be filed?

Tests that you can do for identification.

Test 1:   File a piece with a lesser used part of a file. If the file digs in and cuts the sample is from A or D, or B if in the soft state.

Test 2:   Grind a sample on an abrasive wheel. Look at the nature of the sparks. If the sparks split into stars like a fireworks sparkler the sample is from group B, carbon steel.

Test 3:   Apply a magnet. Stainless steels can be non magnetic. All other iron and its alloys are magnetic. This can be useful in sorting out collections of woodscrews e.g. Brass is an alloy of copper and zinc. Brass often includes small quantities of other metals. Of all the metals brass has the least blunting effect on cutting tools. Bronze, a range of copper and tin alloys, is harder and more weather resistant than even brass. Widely used in 'copper' coins.

   Aluminium is relatively soft. It can be cut and drilled but is rough on the cutting edges of drills and other tools, and soon blunts them. Stainless steel is even more wearing on tool edges than aluminium, but both weather exceptionally well.

Fig 1.5B Information from the kind of sparks

Hand Tools

Most of the tools used for DIY beekeeping purposes are from woodworking practices, hence my recommendations in LIST A include a high percentage of these. The active and discriminating beekeeper, looking for better gadgets often needs to resort to metals and metalwork, and here, some of the workshop tools listed come from this field. Advice to 'buy them as you need them' makes good sense and incurs least damage to the pocket.

LIST A: ESSENTIALS

Screwdrivers,   1/8 in wide (3mm)
(flat blade)   3/16 in wide (5mm)
    ¼ in wide (6.3mm)
¼ pound (100g) hammer
Rip saw
Flexible rule
Hack saw
9" (23cm) try square
Block plane
Sharpening stone
¾" (20mm) wide long chisel
Various knives
"F" clamps
Vice
Hand drill
Cutting pliers
Long nose pliers
Pointed awl
Pozidrive® screwdriver no. 1
Pozidrive® screwdriver no. 2

LIST B: VERY USEFUL

Screwdriver 3/8 in (10mm) wide
½ lb (200g) hammer
Tenon saw
Jeweller's saw
Keyhole saw
Mallet
More clamps
More pliers
Heavy snips
Gaz blowlamp

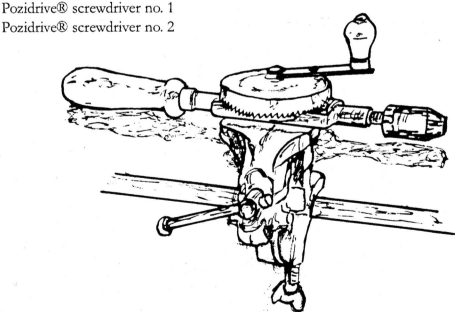

Fig 1.6A When fixed in a bench vice a hand drill is even more useful.

The usefulness of a hand drill can be materially extended if arrangements can be brought about to fix its frame in a bench vice. A metal block can sometimes be made to enable the round, parallel stub of a drill that houses the side knob, to be gripped securely. A suitable wooden block can often be fixed to the underside of the hand drill frame, ready to be fixed into

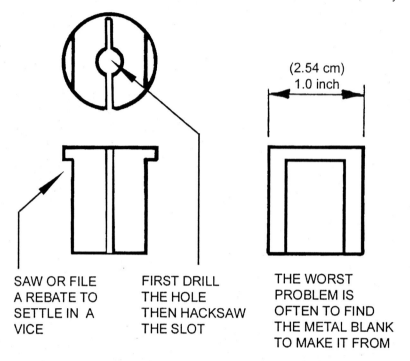

(2.54 cm)
1.0 inch

SAW OR FILE
A REBATE TO
SETTLE IN A
VICE

FIRST DRILL
THE HOLE
THEN HACKSAW
THE SLOT

THE WORST
PROBLEM IS
OFTEN TO FIND
THE METAL BLANK
TO MAKE IT FROM

Fig 1.6B Brass bush to fix a hand drill in a vice.

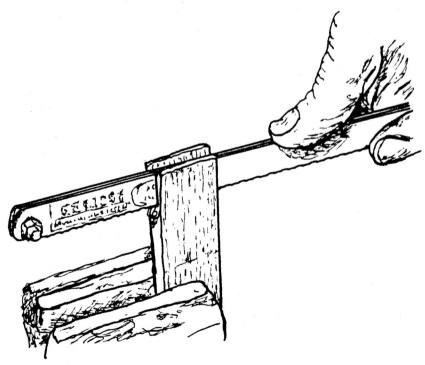

Fig 1.6C A number of blades bolted together. Saw a slot, any width.

the vice. It is a pity that toolmaking companies never supply hand drills with this facility built into the frame. One of my long established resources, it can be used to clean up screws and pins, to rub down and shape wooden dowel rods, and more. It is only when this device is around that unpredicted uses are found for it.

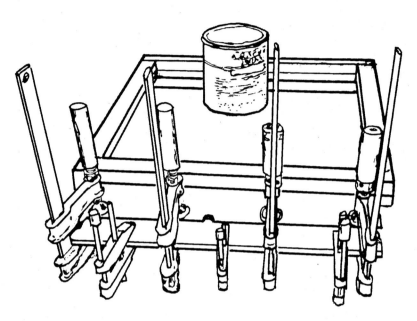

Fig 1.6D Three toolmakers' clamps hold the finger rail of a varroa screen. Four "F" clamps reach further and each hold a batten fast. The tin of paint prevents overbalancing.

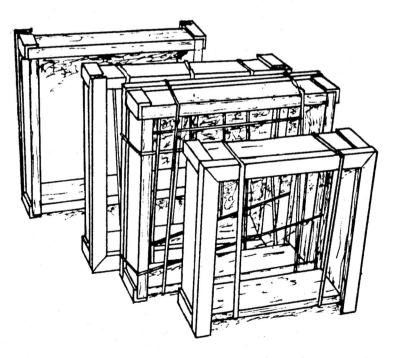

Fig 1.6F A clamping set up for some show boxes using elastic bands

A saw cut of a choice of widths can be made if a hack saw is fitted with more than one blade. I found this to my advantage when confronted with a problem in making a new side for a framed queen excluder. Sawing the lengthwise slot was easy. Two settings of the fence of my table saw and the correct slot width was achieved. The difficulty was how to saw the slots in the ends. They were too deep for the saw table, and I don't care for machine sawing the ends of pieces. I couldn't do it with a hand saw because the blades are too thin for the slot width I needed. The slots required were 0.2 inch (5mm) wide. The bright answer came in the form of five identical hacksaw blades fixed together at each end with 4BA (~3mm) nuts and bolts, and sawn without the hacksaw frame. This gave me the desired slot width and it only needed smoothing with a file.

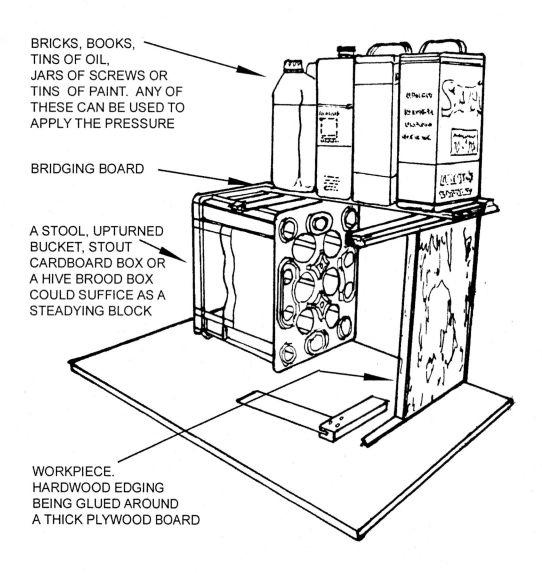

BRICKS, BOOKS, TINS OF OIL, JARS OF SCREWS OR TINS OF PAINT. ANY OF THESE CAN BE USED TO APPLY THE PRESSURE

BRIDGING BOARD

A STOOL, UPTURNED BUCKET, STOUT CARDBOARD BOX OR A HIVE BROOD BOX COULD SUFFICE AS A STEADYING BLOCK

WORKPIECE. HARDWOOD EDGING BEING GLUED AROUND A THICK PLYWOOD BOARD

Fig 1.6E A clamping set-up using weights

Power Tools

Portable Electric Drills

Such an enormous choice is on offer by the tool shops and mail catalogues that one is bewildered about where to start. So how do we choose a power drill? What facilities do we need? Here is a list.

Both my drill guns accept ½ inch (12mm) drills, and can be set to run at either of 2 speeds, one by a gear change and one by a switch. Percussion, hammer and reversing facilities are not needed for beekeeping related projects.

Of all the accessories offered, a cradle type, horizontal drill clamp is recommended. Select a drill gun for which a cradle clamp can also be supplied. Better still, buy them together. Fixed to a wooden baseboard in such a way that it can easily be attached to, and removed from, a bench or Workmate®, it enables the drill machine to turn a grinding wheel, a sanding disc or a buffing pad. Further, the horizontal chuck can be used to hold wooden dowels for shaping or to hold metal pins or cutters. I've often fitted a carbide faced disc to my thus mounted drill gun in order to smooth down uneven timber surfaces. Uneven because they comprise timbers of differing densities. Backed by a rubber sanding pad it does rather well when tidying up joints, even when made of woods of varying hardness.

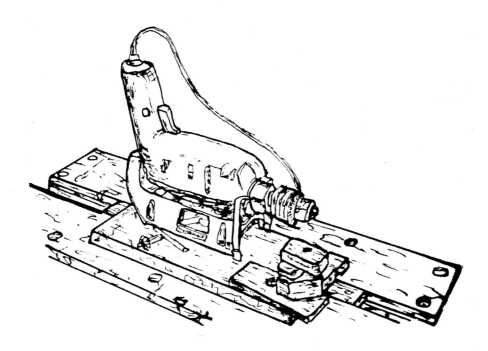

Fig 1.7A Electric drill mounted in a cradle.

Sharpening A Twist Drill

As a youngster in a factory I couldn't sharpen a drill on a grinding wheel very accurately, until a friendly foreman gave me generous fistful of old drills. They all needed attention. By the time I'd sharpened all of them to my satisfaction, I was getting quite good at it. Insistence to wear goggles wasn't energetically applied in those days, but today, one isn't even allowed to use a grinder of any kind, without first attending a certificated grinding course. Courses are available and obviously you would be well advised to follow one before using one for your own health and safety.

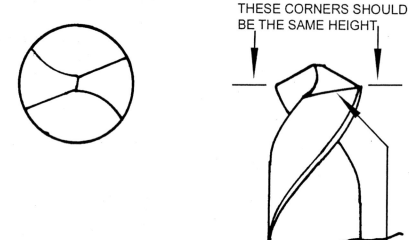

THESE CORNERS SHOULD
BE THE SAME HEIGHT

THIS ANGLE MUST FALL BACK
FROM THE CUTTING EDGE

1.7B Twist drill: precision of symetry is the aim

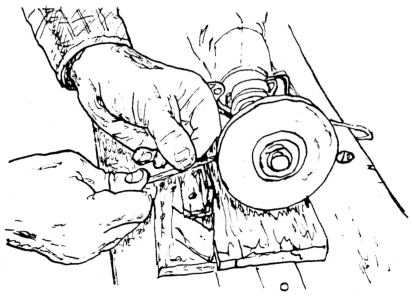

*Fig 1.7C Sharpening A Twist Drill: a twist, a turn and a slight tip up.
All together. Get both sides identical.*

Sharpening a twist drill involves:
1) Turning the drill clockwise about a quarter of a turn during the grind
2) Tipping the drill a little more tail down as you turn it
3) Moving the tail round a little more to the left as you turn it.

When you've got it near enough right turn the drill round 180 degrees and sharpen the other side in the same way. A close inspection is then made in order to ensure that both ground faces are exactly the same. If they aren't, the drill might make a hole a bit bigger than design, or not cut well at all. In common with every other worthwhile skill, practice makes perfect. A rest, fixed closely across the front of the abrasive wheel, often helps to hold the drill point steady. Wear eye protection.

Drills for Wood

The flat type drills for wood are good. Once you've drilled the hole you cannot make it bigger with a bigger flat drill. The guide for the pilot is gone. There is however, a compensating advantage in that the guide point long precedes the main cutting edges, and shows through the remote side long before the main breakthrough. Stop there. Turn the work piece over and drill back from the opposite face. This leaves a clean cut edge on both sides, and avoids leaving a rather jagged, splintered outburst where the drill otherwise breaks through.

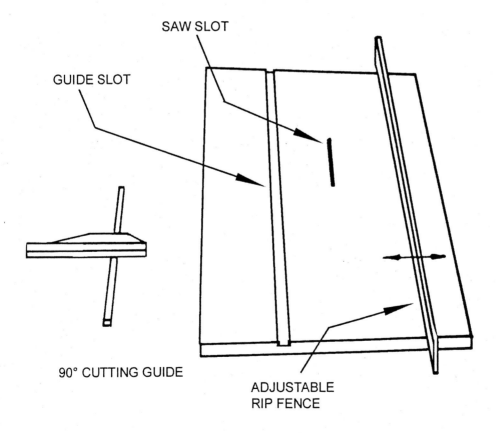

SAW SLOT

GUIDE SLOT

90° CUTTING GUIDE

ADJUSTABLE
RIP FENCE

Fig 1.7D Basic Saw Table top.

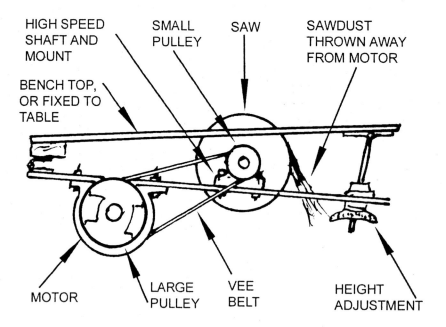

HIGH SPEED SHAFT AND MOUNT

SMALL PULLEY

SAW

SAWDUST THROWN AWAY FROM MOTOR

BENCH TOP, OR FIXED TO TABLE

MOTOR

LARGE PULLEY

VEE BELT

HEIGHT ADJUSTMENT

Fig 1.7E Saw Table: Rise and fall adjustment. Arrange the dust to fall away from the motor. Work passes from right to left.

Circular Saw Bench

Enterprising beekeeping makes much call upon carpentry. The labour entailed is thus reduced, and the speed of production much improved with a saw bench. However, one must be specially careful, and safety conscious, with all machinery, especially powered saws of any kind. Mishaps are better avoided.

A saw bench can be made at home using an electric motor that has been rescued from an old washing machine. A small electric motor with suitable pulleys can usefully drive a 6 inch (15cm) circular saw. One such home made machine served me well for over twelve years. The saw table top was hinged to the garage wall. The legs frame was hinged to that side of the table top away from the wall. At the end of a work session the whole saw bench assembly swung up and was clipped against the wall. The frame now serves as a general work bench (see fig 1.7D and also fig 1.1B).

Table Saw

When the old electric motor eventually failed and proved quite beyond restoration, it was replaced by a 10 inch (25cm) table saw (see fig 1.7F) which stands upon the same fold-up bench-top when in use. Between work sessions this machine hangs on the wall. Neither the table insert suitability for close work nor the 90 degree cutting guide impressed me very much so I made my own.

This machine had several notable differences compared with my previous, home-built saw table:

1) More cutting depth, more power
2) Has some safety facilities built in
3) The saw may be tilted to cut at an angle. Very rarely used
4) Lightweight enough to be lifted up and hung on the garage wall. (Leaves space in the garage for the car).
5) Less table area. It can't guide a board wider than about 10 inches (25cm). So you have to mark it out and feed it past the saw by eye, or consider using a jigsaw
6) Far noisier. (Don't use it too often nearby a neighbour)
7) Needs to be clamped to the bench top, or butted against a fixed stop, or it recedes from the operator during any medium or heavy cuts.

Electric Jig Saw

A jig saw can be very useful for any constructional work, and can, on occasions, prove to be the only convenient answer to some home tasks. A variety of blades are available for cutting different classes of material. Furthermore, be aware of several different designs of blade attachment. A machine from one manufacturer will not accept the blades of another. It is worth while going to the extra cost in order to acquire a variable speed model. A jig saw is particularly suitable for plywood, and can easily deal with very large sheets which can be quite unmanageable by other methods of cutting eg my table saw. It can chug through all sheet timber products up to about 2.0 inches (5cm) thick, and can even cut sheet metals, albeit not very thick. I've even managed to halve several sheets of corrugated iron with a jig saw once. A hair raising experience and not to be recommended.

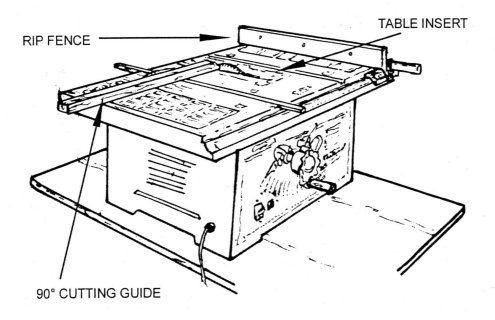

RIP FENCE

TABLE INSERT

90° CUTTING GUIDE

Fig 1.7F 10 inch table saw bench. There is no provision to clamp or bolt it down.

Slot Scraper

Every comb that has been discarded and rendered leaves a frame that needs cleaning up. The slots in the side bars are always filled with wax or propolis. The longer the frame has been in service the blacker and tougher this filling seems to become. Many beekeepers attempt to make a special tool for this scraping task. I describe here how to make your own scraper. One that, I feel, cannot be excelled.

If you make it like this it will cost less than a purchased one. Should you make it well, I can assure you that you will be well pleased with your new acquisition.

Go to a tool shop and buy a stick of silver steel (see chapter 1.5). 0.156 inch or 4mm diameter is just right. This, cut into three equal lengths will give you enough for three blades. I made one, and when I realised how straightforward it was, and felt my upgrade in cleaning out caked up slots, I not only made another two, but made more with blades of slightly different tip widths (see fig1.8A). This was even more useful. I bought a handle too, and later, found another two used handles and pressed them into good use. A 4 inch (10cm) long wooden screwdriver handle is ideal. I first made one scraper complete. I then used the experience to make an even better job of the next two.

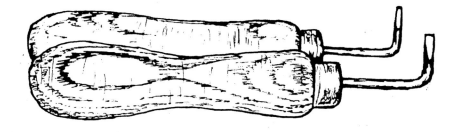

Fig 1.8A Two finished slot scrapers

To set up a mini blacksmith's shop

Most handymen already own the tools needed. You will need (see fig 1.8B):

  Blowtorch
  3 to 5 bricks
  A pot of water
  Pliers
  Vice or anvil
  2lb (1Kg) hammer.
  Hacksaw
  Lighter or matches

As a heat muffle, cement products and concrete are least suitable as bits are liable to split off. Firebrick is the best. Sometimes you see an old broken firebrick fireplace back lying abandoned.

Heat one inch (24mm) of one end of the steel rod in the blow torch flame so that it glows red. Hammer it against the vice or anvil to flatten it. When it is twice as wide as it is thick, you have a shape that will stop it from turning round within the handle. Keep flammable items: paper, rags, wood, etc. out of the way. Hold the blade with the pliers in a recess formed by the bricks and direct the flame into this corner. This helps to concentrate the heat.

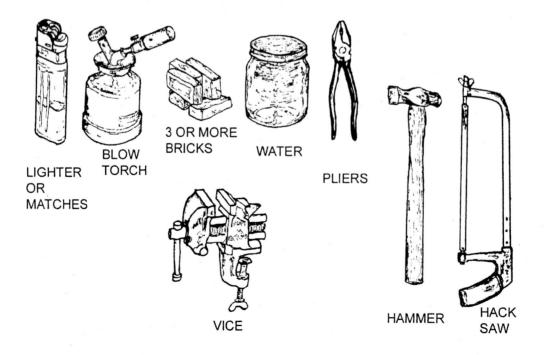

LIGHTER OR MATCHES BLOW TORCH 3 OR MORE BRICKS WATER PLIERS VICE HAMMER HACK SAW

Fig 1.8B Tools required to make slot scrapers

Next step. Similarly heat a half inch (12mm) in from the other end, and quickly grip 0.37 inch (10mm) of the end in the vice and hammer to bend it over to form a right angle (fig 1.8C). The pliers can be a help in this bending, but let the hammer do most of the work. If you find that you've bent more than 0.43 inch (11mm), saw a little off before it is to be hardened. Now heat the bit that you have bent again. This time concentrate on only the end half inch (10mm), and get it even hotter. A bright yellow. Plunge it into the water and waggle it quickly to get rid of the heat. This will make it very hard.

Fixing into the handle

Needed:

Hand or electric drill
epoxy resin (not the rapid set kind)
vice

Drill the handle out to accept the blade flattened end. A tight fit is best. This is because it will need the least resin and will help to hold the blade central while the resin sets. Make the hole deep enough so that only 1.0 inch (25mm) of the blade projects. Two inches (5cm) sticking out is too long and will make your wrist ache when scraping slots.

Fix the handle in the vice, hole facing upward. Mix a suitable quantity of epoxy resin. Push some into the hole you've just drilled. Smear some round the tail of the blade and push the blade into the handle as far as it will go. I found that the resin flows slowly and sinks into the hole such that yet more could be added. Go to bed and leave it to set overnight.

If great care is needed, it will be in the grinding to the final shape and size. Set up a grinding wheel and grind the sides down to about a millimetre thick at the tip. This will produce

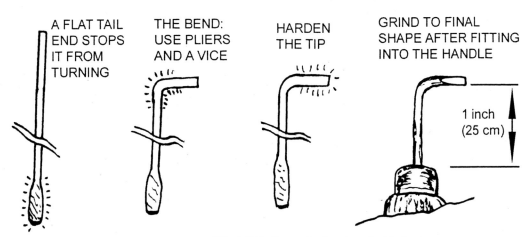

A FLAT TAIL END STOPS IT FROM TURNING

THE BEND: USE PLIERS AND A VICE

HARDEN THE TIP

GRIND TO FINAL SHAPE AFTER FITTING INTO THE HANDLE

1 inch (25 cm)

Fig 1.8C Stages in forming the blade

a lot of sparks, but they are unlikely to burn, and you can wash the dirt off your hands afterwards. Wear eye protection. Don't let the blade get hot. Dip it frequently into the water to cool. If it gets hot enough to start going blue and into brown, then you've already lost some of the blade tip hardness. The back and front are ground similarly and should give a tip width of just under 0.125 inch, or 3mm. Mine measured 0.115 inch (2.92mm). I made my second one slightly wider. I've acquired such a variety of frames that I need several scrapers with different widths.

Frames

Introduction

The frames which house wax foundation are designed to be lifted out of the hive and for manipulation and inspection. The foundation needs to be securely fixed in the frame ready for the bees (see chapter 2.2). The additions of wax, brood and honey can make the frame very heavy.

Wiring and a wedge are normally used together to support the foundation in the frame. Wiring procedures are described below. Techniques for supporting foundation for cut comb are described in this chapter.

Nailing Frames

There is a correct way to nail a frame together, to make it easier to take apart again when it is necessary to fit new foundation, or to repair. This is shown in fig 2.0A. Unless you have good reason otherwise, do it this way. Ten 0.75 inch (19mm) gimp pins are needed. This includes two to fix the wedge.

If you have difficulty in getting the nails in straight, then resort to a Rampin nail inserter. This does help, but check which gimp pins you get. They don't all fit into the Rampin tool.

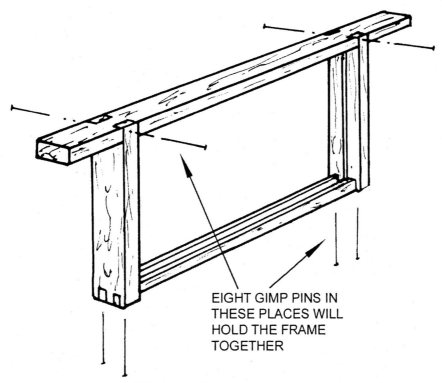

EIGHT GIMP PINS IN
THESE PLACES WILL
HOLD THE FRAME
TOGETHER

Fig 2.0A The correct way to nail frames together

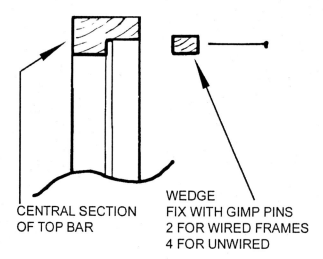

CENTRAL SECTION
OF TOP BAR

WEDGE
FIX WITH GIMP PINS
2 FOR WIRED FRAMES
4 FOR UNWIRED

Fig 2.0B Unwired foundation needs extra support

Foundation for Cut Comb

When fitting unwired foundation its weakness must be recognised. It is that the foundation is inclined to slip out of the wedge and fall away. There is nothing else holding it. Collapses like this will cause a wasted comb form and upset those on either side. A foolproof preparation against this downfall entails bending 0.06 inch (1.5mm) of the top edge of the wax foundation at right angles and arranging it to lie round the wedge. The foundation sheet bends easily if warmed (I use my warming cabinet for this, see chapter 4.5). Fix the wedge with three or four gimp pins.

Place the super containing unwired foundation intended for cut comb in the second position above the queen excluder. This will avert pollen being stored in these combs.

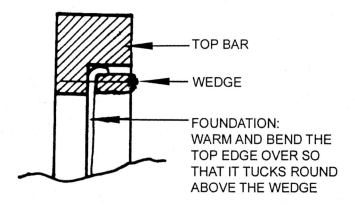

TOP BAR

WEDGE

FOUNDATION:
WARM AND BEND THE
TOP EDGE OVER SO
THAT IT TUCKS ROUND
ABOVE THE WEDGE

Fig 2.0C Yet more support for foundation for cut comb

Marking Hives and Frames

Of all the ways to identify hives, and to mark frames in order to associate each with the hive it came from, and also for the purpose of the frame, say, whether is it unwired, or contains spring honey, or belongs to a friend etc., coloured drawing pins are the most suitable. They can be purchased in eight colours, and of course, there are the regular brass finished ones. If this isn't enough, selections of any two colours can multiply the individual identities. They press into the wood firmly, and rarely come adrift.

On brood frames I use a red drawing pin, pressed into the centre of the top bar, to mark those frames earmarked for withdrawal and later salvage, and white above where I've noted a queen cell. I mark super frames with the colour of the hive that they came out of so that, after extraction, they go back for cleaning up where possible, on to the very hives from which they came.

Placing the Drawing Pins

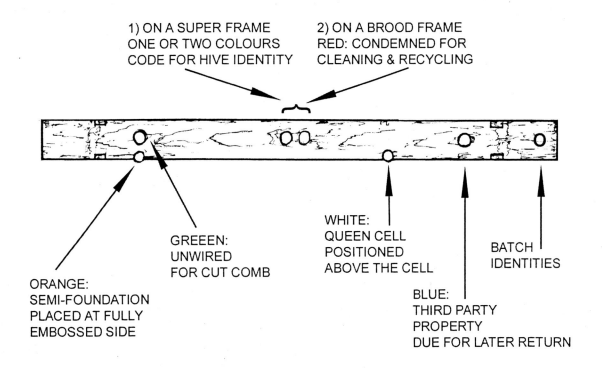

1) ON A SUPER FRAME ONE OR TWO COLOURS CODE FOR HIVE IDENTITY

2) ON A BROOD FRAME RED: CONDEMNED FOR CLEANING & RECYCLING

ORANGE: SEMI-FOUNDATION PLACED AT FULLY EMBOSSED SIDE

GREEEN: UNWIRED FOR CUT COMB

WHITE: QUEEN CELL POSITIONED ABOVE THE CELL

BLUE: THIRD PARTY PROPERTY DUE FOR LATER RETURN

BATCH IDENTITIES

Fig 2.1A Drawing pins on the top bar are reliable markers.
Colour and position are coded to give information.

Wiring the Foundation

Two procedures of installing foundation into frames are in current practice. Pre-wired, and directly wired. There is little difference either way in cost or convenience, but quality and convenience do come into the argument, and these depends upon the workmanship of the constructor more than on other factors.

Pre-wired foundation, which is supplied with the stiffening wire ready embedded into the wax, is appealing to the beginner because the direct wired alternative appears complex, and a jig would also have to be made. Many just want get on with the beekeeping and buy the foundation. Starting this way doesn't preclude a change to the recommended direct wired style at a later date. The quality of the pre-wired foundation sold by the established suppliers is always first class.

In the **directly wired** process the fitting into the frame and the embedding of the wire into the wax, by heating the wire and pressing it into the wax until the melted wax cools and seals over the wire, holding it place, are completed in one operation. However, those who change to the direct wired process, never revert. This is because the direct wired process encourages a straight, flat comb, and avoids the risk of bulges and undulations of comb formation which can complicate comb interchangeability. The forward thinking beekeeper wanting to directly wire the foundation into his frames needs to start with sheets of unwired foundation. He can make his own or he can buy it.

Prewired

There is little economic argument for making a jig for pre-wired embedding, but for those whose enthusiasm for this style, sways a preference, a successful design is shown here.

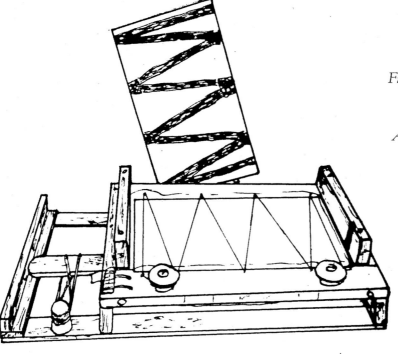

Fig 2.2A Diagonal wiring:
The complete pre-wiring
board in use.
A pressure pad is standing
at the rear.

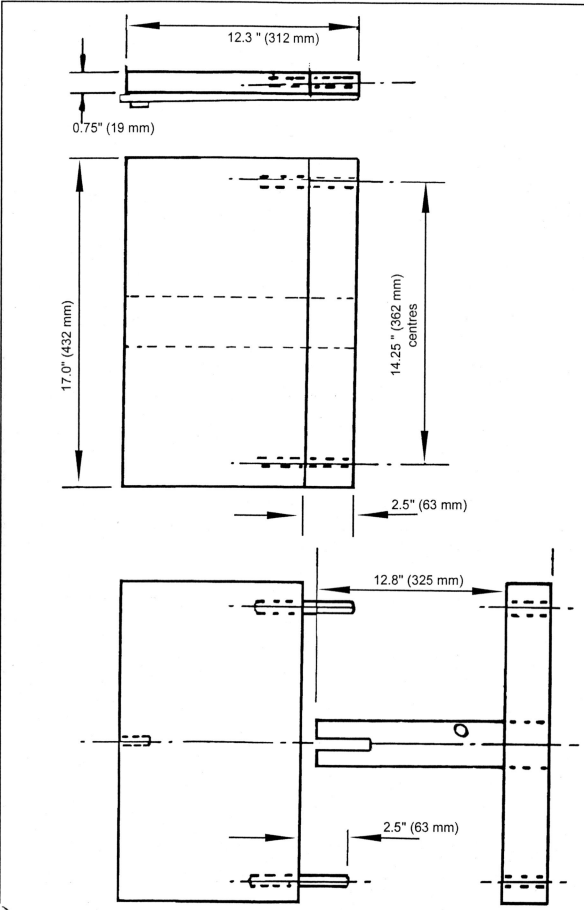

*Fig 2.2B Fitting foundation: the baseboard is split into two parts
that can slide to and from each other.*

To make the wiring jig the baseboard should be completed such that the two parts move against each other freely. The dimensions given are suitable for National deep.

1) Obtain a piece of blockboard 0.75 inch (20mm) thick. Cut a piece 17 inches by 14.9 inches. (432 x 378mm) Drill two holes 5 inches (13cm) deep into a long edge, to accept 0.37 inch (9mm) diameter dowel rods.

2) Cut the board into two; this cut being along the board and 2.5 inches (63mm) from a long edge.

3) Glue two 5 inch (13cm) long x 0.37 inch (9mm) diameter dowels into the bigger piece (The fixed base), so that 2.5 inches (6.5cm) projects. The smaller piece must slide over these projections.

4) The smaller piece (the moving base) has a piece of 0.125 inch (3mm) ply glued on underneath. This reaches and slides on a block at the rear. This is needed to prevent the moving base from tilting and jamming.

Then the linkage (see fig 2.2D) is set up so that the motion of the moving base can be controlled easily by the handle. My model gives 0.5 inch (12mm) of motion from closed to fully open. This is quite enough. If your hoard of nuts and screws etc. in clear glass coffee jars includes one of turned bushes and small metal tubes you are well on the way to piece together the bits necessary to hinge the linkage joints. Using a screw thread as a spindle bearing isn't an ideal engineering principle but it does work as a temporary expedient. One might have to seek more refined mechanical resources in order to reduce backlash in the motion to one's satisfaction.

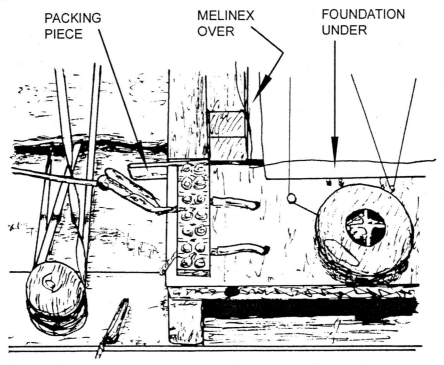

PACKING PIECE

MELINEX OVER

FOUNDATION UNDER

Fig 2.2C Diagonal wiring: The 1mm packing piece is removed to facilitate release.

The pins around which the wiring is looped are made of 0.75 inch (20mm) long nails with their heads cut off. The tips are bent a little, away from the board centre to lodge the wire securely. A 1.0 mm packing piece is placed in the gap during the wiring process. After the wiring has been embedded the packing piece is removed and the gap can then be closed. This enables the loops to be lifted off the forming pins.

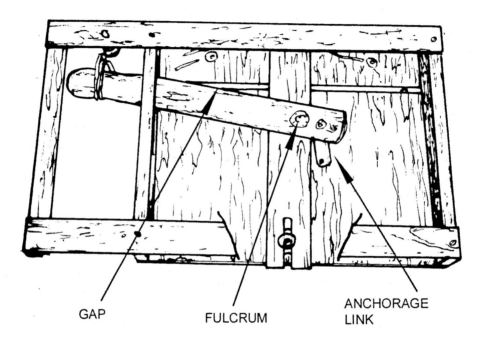

GAP   FULCRUM   ANCHORAGE LINK

Fig 2.2D Diagonal wiring: under the jig. The lever and linkage underneath.

With the gap all but closed, and held a little open by the packing piece, the wire end is first connected to the right hand terminal, passed around the right hand headed nail and round all the forming pins and all the slack pulled out by hand before connecting to the left hand terminal. The wire is not cut from the reel until the embedding is satisfactorily completed. The handle is pulled to stretch the wire until each leg of the wire run is straight. One or more elastic bands are used to retain some tension through the handle. The Melinex is laid over the wires. The pressure plate positioned on top ready for the wire to be embedded in the wax.

Direct Wired

It is recommended from the outset to wire foundation directly into the frames. The fitting incurs little, if any, extra effort, but the gain in straight combs is well worth it. If a comb is free of hollows and bulges it will be the more readily interchangeable. Set a higher intention now. A design for a wiring jig is shown (fig 2.2E), it is adaptable to any common size of frame. I have used mine effectively for several years and have needed no improvement.

The foundation is bought, or made, unwired.

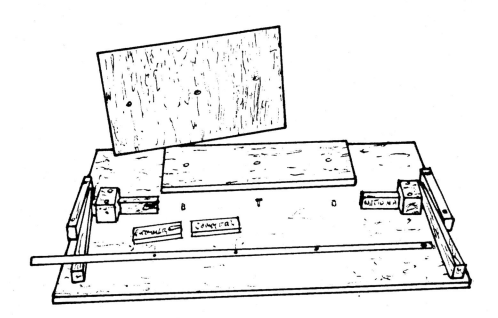

*Fig 2.2E Horizontal wiring: The jig for horizontal direct wiring. Two positioning templates are shown.
The bar at the front is is a mild steel drill jig.*

The baseboard is suitable for Commercial or National Frames. Larger sizes need a wider
baseboard. The baseboard is of 0.75 inch (20mm) blockboard 24inches (61cm) wide and 12
inches (30.5cm) deep. It has three holes accurately positioned with respect to each other in the
central area. It pays to make a drilling jig for these so that the baseboard and any positioning
templates that you make are all drilled identically, and fit. I use a 0.062 inch (1.6mm) drill, and
Sellotape® it to the jig when not in use. The central hole is used to accept a wood screw for
fixing the wiring templates. Dowels 0.25 inch (6.3mm) diameter are glued into the outer two
holes so that they protrude 0.25 inch (6mm). The only other fixations onto the baseboard are
the two outer fences and the two guide blocks, fixed down with two wood screws each.

My push bars are 3.9 inches (9.5cm) long for National frames. I have shorter ones for
Commercial frames. I have even wired Langstroth frames in the jig, but the baseboard really
needs to be a bit wider to start with to accommodate the latter. One of each pair of push bars
is slotted to clear the wire where it threads through outside the side bar.

A positioning template is made for each size of frame to be fitted. Each has three holes
piloted with the drill jig. The central hole is countersunk and is used to fix down the template in
use. Each template should be a sloppy fit in its respective frame. I now have a collection of
these templates.

National	Push bar length.	3.9 inches	(9.5cm)
Commercial	Push bar length	3.0 inches	(7.5cm)
Langstroth	Push bar length	2.1 inches	(5cm)

The frame sides are first fitted with small brass eyelets. These are to restrain the wire at the turns and stop it cutting into the wood. But drill the holes first. The eyelets need fitting only once and last for the life of the frame. The wire traverses across a deep frame from one side to the other four times. A shallow frame only twice. No ups and downs.

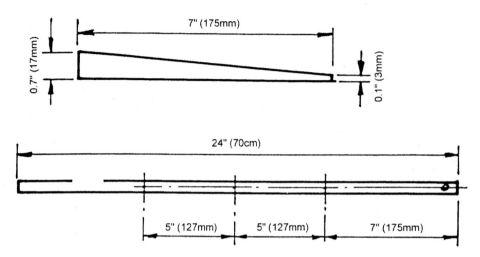

Fig 2.2F (top) Horizontal wiring: wooden wedge
Fig 2.2G (below) Horizontal wiring: drill jig

Make a pointing template from a lino offcut. A piece 2 inches (5cm) wide, and 9 inches (23cm) long will do. Adjust the sizes and hole spacings to suit the frame. I have several different ones to suit the varied frames I've handled.

I look back on the days when I fitted pre-wired foundation. This is the way it was done by my local beekeepers when I started up. The pre-wired sheets of wax, with wire ready embedded relies upon the stiffness of the wire to keep the comb straight. It did a lot of the time, but there were many resulting combs that had bulges and hollows which, in some cases the neighbouring combs followed.

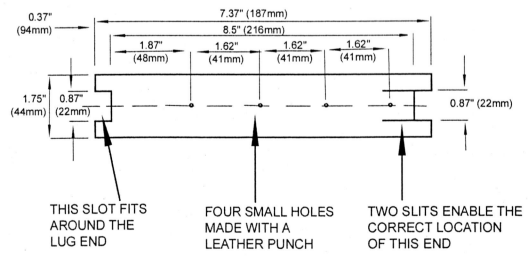

THIS SLOT FITS
AROUND THE
LUG END

FOUR SMALL HOLES
MADE WITH A
LEATHER PUNCH

TWO SLITS ENABLE THE
CORRECT LOCATION
OF THIS END

Fig 2.2H Horizontal wiring: A pointing template for national deep sidebars.
Made from lino

Fig 2.2J Horizontal wiring: lino template in action

In later months when manipulations require certain combs to be repositioned one would often encounter a problem where two combs, each with prominent faces, are needed next to each other, but they need sometimes as much as 0.75 inch (2cm) more space than normal. This will happen to you.

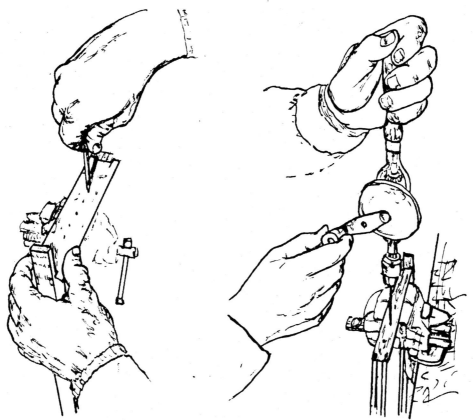

Fig 2.2K Lino template: making the holes

Fig 2.2L Using a hand drill to drill the sidebars

Embedding (Direct wired)

Twenty experts will find twenty different ways to embed the wire to their satisfaction into the foundation. I can only describe the method that I find nicely workable. The width of foundation for the directly wired fittings I cut down so that it doesn't reach the slots in the side bars. [I have no use for these slots. They get filled with propolis and provide excellent crawling galleries for the wax moth larvae. It is just that frames come cheaper with the slots in. If more beekeepers wanted frames without the side slots, such frames would be made to meet the demand.]

Position the foundation into the frame and fix the top by nailing the wedge in. Then set the frame on the wiring jig and thread the wire through the eyelets, on top of the foundation, but without severing the wire from the reel. The far end is fixed down under a nail head. I use a 0.37 inch (10mm) long version of the widely used 20mm gimp pin. With the frame set on the template it is then squeezed together from the sides. The jig does this well and introduces a small stress in the frame. Working from the wire end I pull the wire taut through each eyelet and fix down with two turns round the other tensing nail. This, still without cutting the wire from the reel.

With the wire fitted and now taut, the sideways pressure on the frame is then released.

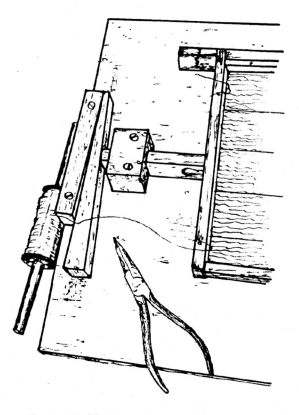

Fig 2.2M Horizontal wiring jig: wire is taut and fixed, now wedges can be removed

Heating the wire

A mains transformer which has a 12 volt secondary that can deliver 5 amps will normally be adequate for all these wiring sizes. A 12 volt car battery will similarly provide enough current. Most car battery chargers deliver about 3 amps. This is not enough.

Either a transformer with a plain 12 volt secondary, or a 12 volt car battery can be used. This voltage can be suitably reduced to get the heating just right, by using some of the wire.

The voltage needs to be adjusted to suit the different wire lengths used in the various frame designs. It is easy to reduce the voltage, but certainly not straightforward to increase it. Fortunately all sizes need less than 12 volts.

Five volts across the wire in the frame is about right for a British National shallow frame, and nine volts is better for the deep frame which uses a longer wire. Even more voltage may be required for the bigger frame designs. These can only be starting figures as other factors come into play, such as the size and material of the wire and ambient temperature. I see no need ever for more than 12 volts.

The wire must be threaded directly from the reel, leaving one end still attached to the reel. Pull more off the reel so that there is a couple of feet of loose wire between the reel and the wire within the frame. Connect one supply clip of your 12 volts, to the far end (ie the end you started threading with) of that wire in the frame, and the other clip to somewhere along this loose length. Start near the reel. The loose length drops (loses) some of the volts. The position of this connection along the loose length of wire must be adjusted to set the correct operating voltage.

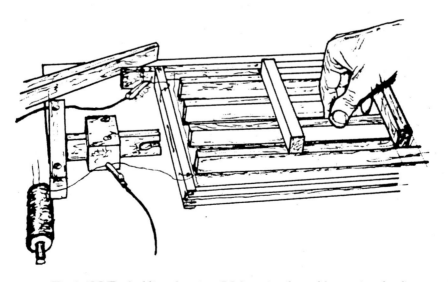

Fig 2.2N Embedding the wire. Voltage is adjusted by moving the clip connection further along the wire, outside the frame.

With the wire positioned, a film of 36gauge (36μM) Melinex® is placed over the wire and a pressure block faced with plastic foam (fig 2.2P) is pressed down on top. The pressure block has the purpose of holding the wire firmly against the face of the foundation. The Melinex® prevents sticking and facilitates release. The current is switched on for 10 to 15 seconds. This time has been found by experience to be about right. If the embedding isn't right, then the voltage, not the timing, should be adjusted. The pressure block can be removed and the Melinex® peeled off almost immediately.

Melinex® will resist very high temperatures. The problem is that although the trade outlets supply enormous quantities, none will sell only 10 square metres. I had to buy 9Kg, and that was an offcut. The other alternative is to look in the kitchenware departments in the high street for roaster bags. Strips of this, cut one inch wide or even narrower to just cover the wire routes, works just the same.

Modest rectangles of this transparent material can be found in food packaging, jellies, pies etc..   You can test for Melinex® using the following tests. Incidentally, look out for Sellotape® branded clear sticky tape, I've also found that Sellotape® passes these tests.

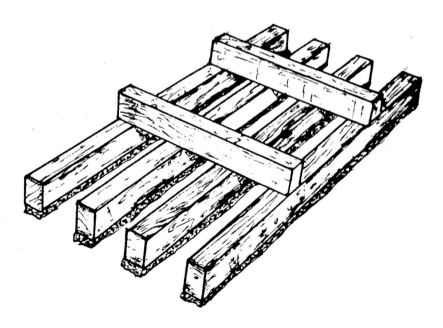

Fig 2.2P Fitting foundation: pressure frame (for holding wire into foundation as it cools and sets) made from scrap timber glued together and faced with polyfoam.

Test 1.   Pull it. If it stretches it is most likely polythene. It's certainly not Melinex®.

Test 2.   Scorch it against an old piece of wood with a hot soldering iron. Make sure that the iron is hot enough to melt solder. Then turn it off and check as it cools, when it will no longer melt the solder, then use it to press the plastic sample hard against an old piece of wood. Solder melts at 183°C, but a soldering iron tip can reach as high as 400°C. This method will set a temperature predictable enough to make a reliable test. If the film survives this test unscathed then it is suitable material for this job.

Fig 2.2Q Fitting foundation: soldering iron.
Heat test: only Melinex® withstands the high temperatures

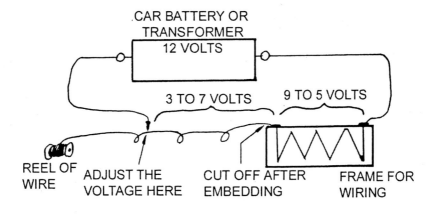

CAR BATTERY OR
TRANSFORMER
12 VOLTS

3 TO 7 VOLTS   9 TO 5 VOLTS

REEL OF   ADJUST THE   CUT OFF AFTER   FRAME FOR
WIRE   VOLTAGE HERE   EMBEDDING   WIRING

Fig 2.2R Adjusting the voltage by effectively lengthening the wire

Cleaning Up 'Wet' Comb

When the extracting is done, the combs are still wet with honey. If bees or ants find them, they will move in. If left, the wax moth will also find them. Sometimes the frames come out of the hive already housing larvae. One solution is to put them back on the hives for the bees to clean, up. I make sure I put the combs back on the hives they come from as good practice for apiary hygiene.

It is of course, quite true: the bees do lick the wet combs over until they are quite dry. However, addressing the following problems will make this a successful operation. Unless someone tells you what the problems are and how to avoid them, you must learn them the hard way, so, read on:

Problem 1) The rich fragrance of honey that these combs release is asking for robbing to start if the combs are laft near the hives carelessly.

Answer 1) As when putting on a feed, wait until dusk, or earlier if the flying has stopped. Then put the wet combs on. Cover the boxes of wet combs, top and bottom, with flat, ply or hardboard boards in order to contain the smell of honey until immediately before putting on. Leave one of these boards across the top, under the roof, for a better seal.

Problem 2) A strong colony sometimes still brings in nectar in late summer and stores it in the lowest super that you've just put on for cleaning up.

Answer 2) Set an empty box to function as a spacer between brood and the wet supers. This will encourage them to store it in the brood box. Make quite sure that there are no gaps that will give access to robbers.

Problem 3) The wet combs, normally spaced, when cleaned up are usually found sporadically braced together in several places across the comb faces.

Answer 3) Space them wider apart. Find a convenient way of spacing eight or nine combs equally across the width of the box. Try wide spaced metal ends, or alternate narrow and wide. This has a similar wider spacing effect.

Problem 4) Robbing.

Answer 4) Use only strong colonies for cleaning wet comb in supers.

It takes several days for a clean up to dryness, depending upon the strength of the colony, and of course, how many combs you are stacking on. Ten days will give you a starting figure, for two supers on a strong colony. Take the combs off with clearing boards and porter escapes, as when taking off honey supers. If you take them off in the early morning, following a cool night, you may not need escapes at all.

Tidying Up Used Frames

I put old combs into my solar panel, frames and all, to melt out the wax, but first take off the metal ends and any drawing pins. Frames straight out of the solar panel may well have been divested of most of their wax; they have had the advantage of any tiny moth larvae, or eggs still languishing in dark corners, eradicated by baking; but the frames still look mucky. They are mucky; with propolis; with pupa skins and with honey and caramel.

If you've only a few dirty frames, first give them a soak in a bucket of water for ten minutes, this dissolves any honey and makes them less sticky in any subsequent handling. Then leave them to dry. When dry, scrape them clean with a knife,

Dissolving debris in boiling caustic soda

A batch of fifty or more sticky frames presents a prolonged scraping task; quite rough on the hands too. In this case a caustic boil-up is worth considering (please refer to the Health and Safety section page *v*, and notes p 46. A four minute dip can remove all traces of honey, wax, propolis etc from every part of the frame. Even from underneath the wedges.

A 25 litre, open top drum is filled with boiling water. The domestic hot water system can deliver at around 50degC. (Not the morning after a late bathing session.) This can be boosted to a close approach to boiling in saucepans on the domestic cooker. If the drum is first stood

Fig 2.4A Frames in a bucket: Dissolving away any residual honey.
The spring clip is to weigh the frames down.

upon bricks or a purpose made metal stand, a propane camping stove can be set up underneath to maintain the temperature. This operation is best performed screened from any wind. A thermometer for wax is a decided help to keep the temperature at over 90 degC.

Add the caustic soda gingerly; about 20g at a time, as the job progresses. A scum usually forms on top of the water. Much of this can be scooped off with an old tea strainer. What scum remains can be prevented from depositing on the frames on withdrawal by swirling the potion around first. A further 50g of caustic can be added if the scum builds up too much.

The frames are inclined to bob up by floatation. They can be held down if you make up a special block of wood to fit roughly the top of the drum. This can be additionally weighted down if necessary. After the four minute immersion, remove the frames and rinse them with water.

Safety recommendations (see also the Health and Safety Preface page *v*):

1)   Avoid splashing or tainting your skin or clothes with the caustic solution. Wear old gloves and clothes. Wear eye protection.
2)   Work on your own. Don't handle boiling water while someone else is working in the area.
3)   Do not dump too much caustic soda at a time into boiling water. It causes a violent upheaval.
4)   Make sure that the drum is stolidly supported.
5)   Use rubber gloves to handle the wet frames.
6)   Leave the drum to cool before emptying.

If caustic soda is deemed too vigorous, a potion of washing soda, bleach and detergent can be tried, but very hot water will still be needed.

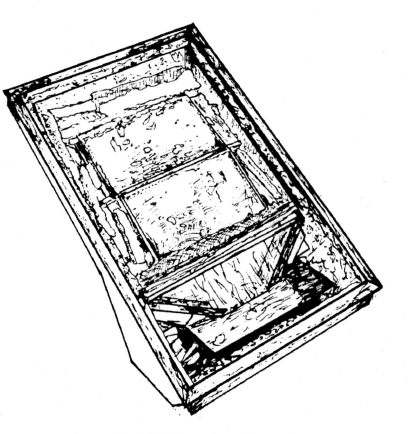

Fig 2.4B Frames in a solar panel

Metal Ends

Metal ends are an essential adjunct to the frames which are used in National hives. They have an additional use in spacing the frames the correct distance apart for the bees. Metal ends have an advantage when used on DN/1 and DN/2 type frames; those frames no part of which exceeds 0.875 inch (22mm) wide. I say this because, with the metal ends removed, these frames may be stored up to eighteen in a British National box. Hoffman frames, for all their advantages, will not store compactly like this.

They need special attention for cleaning before re-use.

Just getting them off the frame lug ends can be quite rough on the fingers. They're often propolised so hard on to the frames that you need a pickaxe to dislodge them. This difficulty is considerably reduced by using a suitable old table knife to jab along the top of the top bar, but under the metal end (fig 2.5B), before the frames are lifted out of the boxes. This cracks half the attachment and ensures a much easier pulling off. I have a favourite old table knife I use for this, its blade is ideal, thin and springy.

These metal ends are favourite areas for the bees to deposit oodles of gungey gum. I've seen them buried in compacted layers of the hardened propolis. For too long I begrudged my time sorely when scraping each surface of each metal end free of propolis with a small knife, and close under a lamp. It roughened my fingers, and was a long, boring and thankless job. Eventually, after many years I found a better solution (see chapter 2.4).

Attempts over the years to dissolve the propolis in boiling water; in an old saucepan; with detergent; with ammonia; with soda; and then with domestic cleaners were all quite ineffectual. They all produced dirty, hot water. None got much of the propolis off. I had avoided trying out caustic soda for some years in the belief that it would take off the tin plate. It didn't. Caustic soda does incur handling hazards though, and needs respect (see Health and Safety

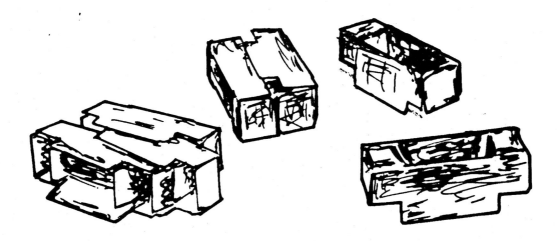

Fig 2.5A   Metal Ends

preface page *v*, and also notes p 46). But so does boiling water, and we use this daily for many purposes e.g. making tea. So, get an old enamelled saucepan. I got mine for a song at a local car boot sale. Avoid aluminium for this purpose. Caustic etches holes in aluminium wares. Later, I also bought a wire basket which fitted into the saucepan nicely.

A little caustic soda in boiling water dissolves the propolis clean away. Be careful not to tip very much at a time into the hot water. It can almost explode. Follow the safety guidelines given in chapter 2.4.

Rinse the ends in clean water and set them out singly on old newspaper sheets to dry. If this takes too long, just spread them out to dry, but separate the twos and threes that have become interleaved. This traps water for a long time and encourages rust. The only individual attention needed at any time is now. Sort out any bent or broken ones, and re-treat or scrape any still harbouring any clinging blobs of propolis.

Fig 2.5B With the top propolis cracked using a knife, the frame is easier to lift, and the metal end easier to remove.

Making and Using Semi-Foundation

In this chapter I describe a low-cost method of foundation making which should appeal to many do-it-yourself workers who prefer to recycle their own beeswax. Semi-foundation is a wax foundation sheet, embossed one side only.

I first describe the making of a forming tray, used to make a suitable tray out of silicon rubber (SR). Then this is used to mould a wax sheet which will be embossed on one side with worker pattern. This is semi-foundation. This will be followed with a description of how it can be used in a hive.

Silicon Rubber (SR)

Silicon Rubber (SR) is ideal for the casting, or moulding, of beeswax. This is because the release, the separation when cool, is so easy. Its application for moulding candles is well established. It can be similarly exploited for the making of foundation.

SR costs about 50p per cubic inch, or approximately £9 per pound, or roughly four times the value of beeswax if you like an inflation proof guide. It does not have a high tensile strength, and does not yield to elongations of five times its natural length like elastic bands; ten percent is a lot nearer actuality. But these are no limitations for what we want, and its other qualities are ideal for our purpose. Furthermore, it can usually be repaired. Suppliers (see suppliers list) are extremely helpful and it is wise to follow their recommendations, e.g. in weighing out and in thorough mixing. The SR tray that I made for National deep foundation weighs 770g. That for the shallow version has a thicker base and weighs 800g.

You will need:

1 Silicon rubber. The necessary
   catalyst is usually included
   in the price.

2 Release agent. (This is for the
   wooden surfaces).

3 Cab-0-Sil. Powder additive for
   thixotropic properties
4 Plastilene

5 Breathing mask

Fig 2.6A Start by maing a wooden forming tray with a 2" (5 cm) gap one end

The thixotropic additive is a light, fluffy powder. When the full amount is mixed in, the runny rubber converts into a paste which defies gravity. Verticals and arches stay where they are put, but the other properties of SR are unaffected. I am told that this powder is carcinogenic so I bought an inexpensive breathing mask for use when handling it.

Making the Wooden Forming Tray

A sheet of worker foundation, about 2 inches (50 mm) larger in length and width than the final size needed, must be acquired. Then a wooden forming tray (fig 2.6A) is made using this as a template so that the final foundation will be a size larger than needed, and can be cut down neatly to size.

I bought some Commercial deep foundation (15.4 inches x 9.5 inches (39.2 x 24.1cm), with the British National deep final size (13.4 inches x 8 inches (34 x 20.3cm) in mind.

A 2 inch (5cm) gap is left at one end of the tray through which the surplus wax is ultimately poured away. I glued the fences to the base in order to prevent any prospect of SR, when liquid, seeping under them.

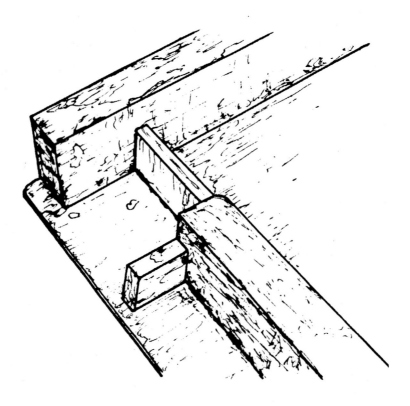

Fig 2.6B Close off the gap temporarily

Pouring the Rubber to Make the Base of the Tray

Before pouring the prepared SR into the wooden tray, the gap is blocked off temporarily with a piece of scrap wood, and sealed at the base with Plastilene. Then the tray is treated on all its inner surfaces with release agent, and allowed to dry.

The wax foundation sheet is set down flat into the forming tray, and the edges sealed all round by pressing in a small wedge of Plastilene. SR does not stick to Plastilene. SR does however, stick fast to almost everything else, but luckily, not to beeswax. Cut a piece of muslin to the size of the foundation, and put it aside ready for use. Set the tray level, with a spirit level if you have one. Mix the necessary catalyst drops into 350 to 500 g of SR (the thixotropic additive is not needed at this stage) and, when mixed, pour out onto the face of the wax foundation. It will spread all over the foundation surface without much help, but you need to spread it evenly using a disposable piece of card. Then lay the muslin onto the surface of the SR to cover the whole area; and make sure that it is rubber 'wetted'. It must sink into the SR without trapping air pockets. Leave it undisturbed to set (about 24 hours, but see the manufacturers' instructions) When thoroughly set, the SR sheet may be peeled off and the wax foundation and Plastilene removed.

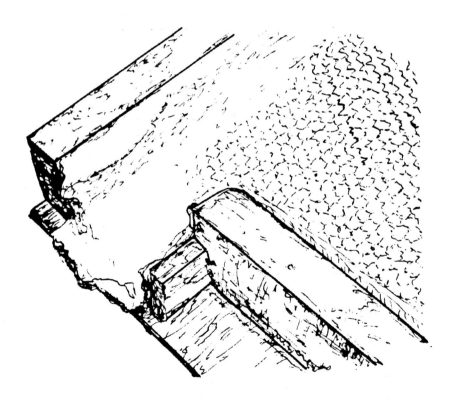

Fig 2.6C The outlet duct in Silicon Rubber

51

Forming the Fences of the SR Tray

The gap in the wooden tray may now be opened up and modified so that a SR outflow duct can be made that will direct the surplus molten wax away. It will still work, however, if you simply leave a gap.

Treat any newly exposed woodwork with release agent. Set the SR sheet, with all traces of Plastilene removed, back into the wooden tray, this time with the embossed side uppermost. 400g of thixotropic SR can now be prepared by mixing in the catalyst and then stirring in the full recommended quantity of thixotropic powder. This mix will now stay wherever it is put. It will not flow at all. Butter it on all round the inner surfaces of the walls. Also form the outlet duct.

The walls are best tapered making them thicker at the base. The SR thickness should be about. 0.12 inch (3mm) at the top, and 0.37 inch (10mm) at the base, where it will stick fast to the surface of the SR base, wherever it is placed. The sloping edge will later enable the wax sheet to be lifted out a little more easily. When the shaping is done to satisfaction, it must be left alone to set. Leave it 50% longer than the recommended set time. Only then is it wise to prise it out of the wooden tray. It is a good idea to keep the wooden tray and use it to store the more valuable, and more vulnerable SR tray.

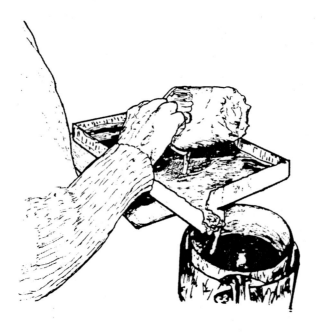

Fig 2.6D   Pour the wax on, run it round and pour off the surplus

Making the Wax Semi-Foundation Sheets

Sit the SR tray on a plain plywood board of about the same size, and hold them together horizontally. Its wooden forming tray will suffice, held upsaide down, with the SR tray outlet duct over the pot of molten wax. The plywood board/tray is to hold the floppy tray flat. Pour a pint (0.5 litres) of molten wax onto the SR tray. Ideally this is done fairly briskly so that the wax flows straight into all four corners, but sloshed too fast, the wax will flood over the sides. It is best to start first time by taking it gently. After all, the wax can always be recycled if the first result is imperfect. About five seconds and the surplus wax must be poured away, back into the pot. This, before it sets through to the top surface.

If it looks a bit thin, pour some more wax on, and again run the surplus away. In this way more thickness can be achieved. With further operations I produced a range of 50 to 80 grams for the National deep 13.4 inch x 8 inch (334 x 203mm) size. When it has suitably cooled, after about five minutes, the new wax sheet of semi-foundation can be peeled off fairly easily. Neither water nor release agents are needed. I cut off the turned up edges all round with a big pair of scissors while they are still warm. The thickness and the production rate are limited largely by how fast the heat can be lost from the tray between castings. Three techniques can be brought into play in order to speed production:

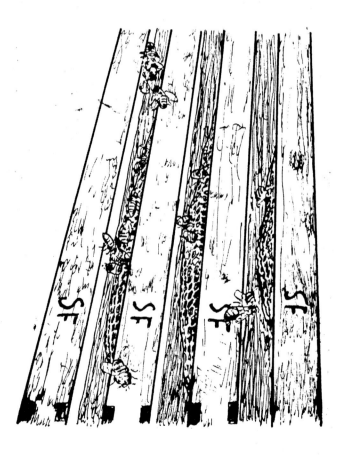

Fig 2.6E Semi-foundtion, drawn and used by my bees. The fully embossed side is sometimes drawn to extend into a neighbouring space

1 Cool the tray by sandwiching between cooler wooden or metal plates.
   What about an ice, or cold water bag?
2 Pour the wax at a lower temperature.
3 Use two trays alternately. Maybe one for deeps and one for shallows?

Finally cut to size with a knife round a sheet metal template 13.4inches x 8 inches (34 x 20.3 cm) for my National deep size.

In the Hive

Should a sheet of semi-foundation be wired into a frame in the same way as full foundation and then placed into a hive, the bees will draw it into comb. The embossed side will have an orderly array of cells, each in line and set upon the next, such as we are all ever amazed to behold. However, the other side will not be so neat and tidy. It will get drawn alright, but haphazardly, with no straight rows at all, and quite often with all drone size cells. Furthermore, my bees set about drawing the embossed side first, completed and filled it with nectar before a third of the flat side was drawn. Nevertheless, it was nearly all drawn and filled with honey and duly sealed over.

Some Embossing Print Through

It may be observed that the thinnest sheets made this way show some of the embossing pattern on the ostensibly flat side. When these sheets were drawn there was a strong tendency for my bees to follow this pattern. This was not a great success because that foundation thin enough to be fully effective in this way was too thin to stand up to reasonable handling. Those thicker sheets, from 60g (British National, deep) upward, reveal progressively less print-through, and the cells drawn on the flat sides progressively lose registration. Sheets of 80g and more lose all registration, and mine often were mainly of drone form on the flat sides. All is not lost though, because there are further procedures that are worth subjective assessment.

Back to Back

Then came the idea of mounting two sheets in a frame, back to back. Four National deep, DN/1 frames were each fitted with two of these sheets, flat sides together. First the empty frames were wired using eyelets, and the wire pulled tight. The sheets were then mounted against the wire and fixed with the wedge at the top, and set between the bottom bars. I must admit, this was a bit of a squeeze. The wire was heated and this seemed to fix the sheets together. No attempt was made to register the embossed patterns in natural, mutual placement. All these frames were drawn, filled and capped, and by this time they were indistinguishable from the normal, sealed combs. The composite foundation here and the resulting drawn comb, seemed a bit heavy, but the old maxim still stands. You get all the wax back, and more.

Easier ways of achieving double faced assemblies come to mind as they entail first fitting and wiring a semi-foundation sheet into a frame as if it were normal foundation, and then attaching a second semi-foundation sheet to its flat side,

1 with metal clips.
2 with a small run of molten beeswax.

The second idea above was tried with success. I had a second sheet cut down ready, poured some hot wax on, and pushed the second sheet down upon it without delay. It stuck on, and became fully integrated when being drawn.

One Sided Frames to Suit

Those who would prefer to mount each of the semi-foundation sheets singly into their own frames would take a special interest in the results from this method, which uses a special, simple, half frame. This is similar to that shown in fig 2.7D, but its width is 0.6 inches (15.2mm) and has about three notches in the top bar to allow bees access the the areas above and below. As there is no wedge the top and bottom wires should be set within 0.3 inches (8mm) of the top and bottom bars respectively.

These frames were set close spaced into a super box, all facing one way. I set banks of 14 and 16 in different hives and filled the remaining spaces with normally fitted standard shallow frames. They were all drawn, filled with honey and sealed. That is, all of them on one side only. The flat sides weren't even drawn. The resulting space efficiency was about 65%, where for natural comb placement it would be about 80%.

Bees Won't be Guided

Several schemes were considered, purposed to guide the bees to start drawing the flat side in neat registration with the embossed side. Attempts were made to see if the message of comb pattern can be passed somehow from one side of the semi-foundation to the other. Two framed sheets of semi-foundation were each perforated over a large area with 1.0mm pin holes. The bees faithfully filled all these holes with wax. Well, I wasn't expecting too much! Let's start again.

Further trials were devised with semi-foundation, each presenting to the bees an edge of semi-foundation sheet, similar to that edge when the bees are making wild comb. One with a variety of vertical slits of different width, and two with holes of different diameters, but all big enough for a bee to get through, with access to an edge. An array of 10, 15 and 22mm diameter holes with a range of spacings was made in two semi-foundation sheets.

All these were inserted into hives where building was expected. The workers closed most of the holes as expected, but no trace of registration or order reached the flat sides.

Furthermore, even the skins of wax that closed the holes showed no sign of continuing the embossed pattern.

The very thinnest sheets have tiny triangular holes right across the face, where the wax fails to skin across the peaks of the hexagon centres. These holes all get filled and the whole sheet gets fully drawn on both sides. However, the bees go for the deeply embossed sides first, and are inclined to draw that side almost fully before starting on the lesser impressed side.

Single or Double?

Single mounting is the easiest and most economic way. A thin semi-foundation sheet can be wired into any standard frame in just the same way as wiring commercial foundation.

Double mounting, that is, fixing two such sheets back to back into a frame, has the advantage of presenting well formed embossing to the bees on both sides, but doesn't fully appeal for the following reasons.

1   Two sheets are needed for each frame.
2   More wax is needed to start with, but this is not lost.
3   A method of attaching the two sheets and of wiring them must be adopted.

Obervations from Single Mounting

In 1994/95, I used over 60 semi-foundation sheets in brood boxes, supers and to house swarms.

When single mounted full frames were set into a super box with the deeply embossed sides all facing the same way these sides became drawn so extensively that some areas intruded into the spaces that would normally have been taken up by the neighbouring combs. Here and there the opposite facing flat faces did not get drawn at all. Most did have large drawn patches though this is not a great problem because this deep comb can be readily cut down to normal depth in the uncapping process. This effect can be reduced by setting deep embossings either facing each other, or facing drawn comb, and by setting vestigial or non-existent embossings facing each other.

But we can do better than this by mixing new semi-foundation with drawn comb in the supers and by fitting a higher proportion of drawn comb in brood boxes. I fitted these exclusively for two years.

Is Foundation Needed?

Before manufactured foundation became available, those beekeepers who wished to use frames got the bees to make comb within the frames by using "starters". Bees do need at least a starter if they are to build predictably placed combs. Starters are either shaped top bars each with a thin ridge along the lower edge, which is coated with wax; or thin wedges of beeswax, usually fashioned by hand, and fixed or melted onto the top bar undersides. Small hexagon sculpted rollers were sometimes used to impress wax sheets into little strips of starter 'foundation', before 'sheet' foundation became commercially available.

The bees start working on the lower edge and produce comb like a curtain, straight down until it reaches the bottom bars. If you wish to see it you can easily prepare one of your frames like this, and comb will be made without foundation at all. Or you can fit foundation of any smaller size, and the bees will continue making it, but always downwards.

Should you for any reason be limited to making only one silicon rubber forming tray you will have two options, deep, or shallow. For a tray big enough to make deep semi-foundation some of the sheets can be cut into halves lengthwise, these two halves to be fitted into shallow frames. They will cover about 60% of the depth. The bees will fill in down to the bottom. Be aware of where the wiring comes though, if you wire horizontally into the frames.

All beekeepers need a source of foundation. Those who cannot buy manufactured foundation due to cost or geographical limitations must consider making their own. Each beekeeper has a source of wax. Flat beeswax sheets can be made easily as shown in fig 2.6D, and fitted into frames will be drawn readily into comb; if embossed foundation is needed, a compromise from the ideas suggested here may provide the answer.

Although I have described fully the problems, many quite satisfactory combs have been produced using semi-foundation.

Splitting the Honeycomb

I introduce a method of separating two halves of a honeycomb, right down the middle of the central membrane so that the two parts can be separated, each half intact. This can be before or after extraction, so that one can choose whether to include the capped honey.

Many would regard this achievement as quite useless. It is positively useless. Nevertheless, I must add at this point that producing a close approach to a perfect one pound (454g) block of beeswax is also claimed as useless. Yet the one pound block has attained a high profile position as a competitive class in all the leading honey shows and most others. Both exercises are tests of one's resources and skills. Would splitting the honeycomb make a far better honey show class? There is a lot more beekeeping in it.

For me this was an interesting exercise (in conjunction with my studies of semi-foundation (chapter 2.6), which showed me that each side of the foundation is worked separately and can be split into two entities. I found that when two sheets of semi-foundation

Fig 2.7A Three split frames nestling among the others

are used back to back, the centres of the hexagons one side do not necessarily coincide with the interstices of of three cells the other side, but follows the foundation put in. This does not appear to matter to the bees or affect the production of the honey.

One must start with a wooden frame which is itself separable into two identical halves. I illustrate the half frames that I made (see figs 2.7B, C and D). Each half is fitted with foundation. I used semi-foundation, which is embossed only on one side, but this is not regarded as a necessity. Ordinary foundation can be used. I wired each into its own half frame. The two halves were then clasped together with two rectangles of plastic film slipped between the two to span the whole of the foundation and the frame. It was found that the bees make some holes in polythene. Clingfilm gets torn to shreds. Only Melinex®, or no doubt its

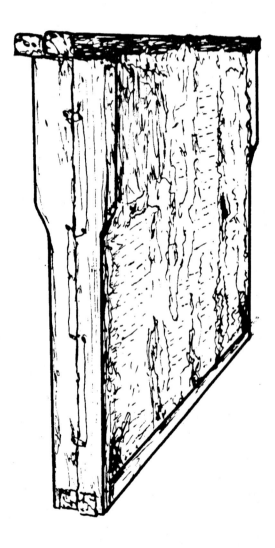

Fig 2.7B Drawn split comb in a frame before separation

equivalents, withstands the bees attentions. They are literally unable to nibble it. If two sheets of film are slipped between at the start, then the two halves come apart without any prising or comb flexing, and the films can then be peeled off the backs of their respective half combs. The half frames are fixed together by twisting short pieces of wire around the pairs of gimp pins on the side bars which come together.

The composite frame is then installed in a super, filled, capped, and also extracted if required, and cleaned up before the halves are separated. Although a sheet of Melinex® can be peeled away from wax it doesn't come away readily from the whole surface in one go; the comb and the film each staying flat during the separation.

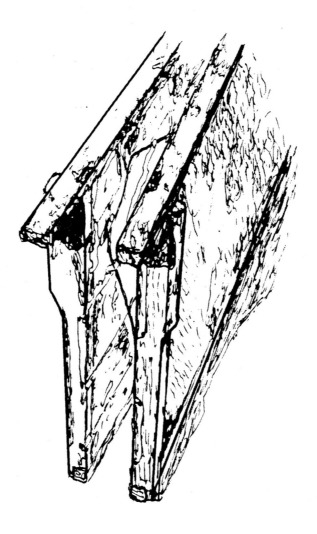

Fig 2.7C The Two halves separated

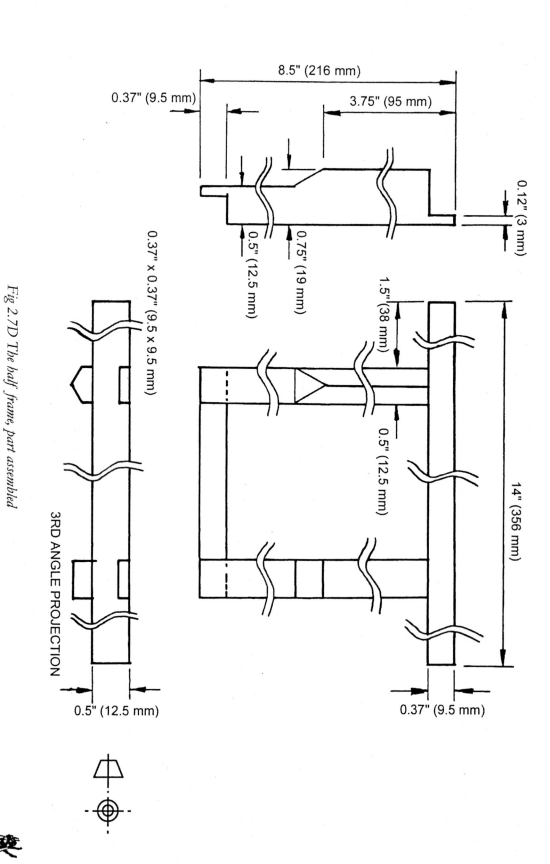

Fig 2.7D The half frame, part assembled

3RD ANGLE PROJECTION

Making Foundation

Every beekeeper has a source of beeswax, and, with time, the newcomer sees the stock of wax build up. Meanwhile he needs to buy more and more foundation. This seems such a ridiculous state of affairs when he already has more than sufficient basic material. Why not use it and make his own foundation? This can appeal to some.

I describe a well established method of pressing a whole sheet from melted wax in one operation between fibreglass embossing faces (Hamer, 1993.) To retain good domestic harmony some of the operations are best carried out away from one's living quarters: somewhere where the strong smell of polyester resin can be tolerated.

What is needed for the Foundation Press

This press consists of a wooden frame, and two, one upper and one lower, polyester laminate templates for embossing the wax. Firstly you need to decide the size of foundation you need to make, maybe starting with a press for a smaller size first. A small press is easier to use, and the experience gained will pay off well when you make a bigger one. Then follow the method below for making the laminates.

The Foundation Press

The dimensions given are to produce the most popular size in Britain for such a press, the National deep ie to fit in National brood boxes, 13.5 x 8.0 inches (343 x 204mm). The original form, used as a master, is bigger, at 15.5 x 9.5inches (394 x 242mm). This leaves a margin all round which can be cut off, sometimes selectively to minimise faults. The trimmings can always be recycled. For other, larger, sizes of foundation a larger size press will be necessary; for smaller sizes you have the choice either to trim the foundation and recycle the excess, or to make another, smaller, foundation press.

Fig 2.8A Foundation Press:The Complete Press

The Laminate

What you will need (suppliers are listed p iii):

1) A sheet of commercially made, unwired foundation, in pristine condition. Commercial size
2) Fibreglass sheet. Enough to give 2 pieces , each 16.5 x 10.5 inches (420 x 270mm). This is to prevent the prominent hexagons from pulling out.
3) Polyester resin. Car repair kit or The Fibreglass Shop, but always respect the supplier's instructions
4) Catalyst to suit. This is supplied with the resin
5) Two sheets of glass, each 19.5 x 13.5 inches (500 x 340mm). These dimensions for the glass are not critical. Rub all the edges smooth with a sharpening stone as soon as you get it. It may save you from a nasty cut. The heavier, plate glass is preferable if you have a choice
6) Two pieces of cellophane, about the same size as the glass. A roll can be obtained from leading stationers. Polythene can be used, but this stretches and the distortions won't restore
7) Wax release agent
8) Weighing scales and a 1cc graduated syringe for measuring
9) Mixing containers. Use glass, enamel or stainless steel, not polystyrene mixing pots. They melt and start leaking before you can complete the pouring. The most suitable are the disposable waxed cardboard pots.
10) Plastic gloves
11) Metal scraper. This helps to spread the resin
12) Brush and acetone to wash it with

Procedure

1) Make up about 300g of resin for National deep/brood box size
2) Apply a film of release agent on one face of each of your glass plates.
3) Cut the fibreglass and cellophane pieces to size, ready for use.
4) Build up the layers in the order shown (fig 2.8B), centrally placed on the glass plate, finishing with the second glass plate on the top. Make sure that the foundation lays flat against the face of the glass plate.
5) Ensure that the first application of resin is just enough to cover all across the whole foundation face and fills all the cell depressions. 60g is about right. If possible prevent the resin from creeping under the edges of the foundation. Let it flow about half an inch beyond the edges. It is worth the trouble to release air bubbles which seem to have an affinity for staying in the cells. Dab them with a stiff brush. You will need to wash   the brush out with acetone afterwards.
6) Place the fibreglass sheet over the whole of the foundation area and half an inch beyond the edges, starting from one edge with a rolling motion, aiming to avoid any air pockets.
7) Then apply another application of resin, enough to fully encapsulate the fibre. About 80g. Spread it evenly. Release any air bubbles that remain.

8) Next lay the cellophane on from one end to trap minimum pockets of air. Push any residual air out by stroking it towards the edges.

9) The second glass plate goes on the top.

10) Having completed this sandwich, the whole assembly is turned over, and the bottom glass, now on top, can be carefully prised off. This will reveal the reverse of the foundation surface. Clean the glass.

11) The second side can then be built up in the same way, finishing with a weight on top. Mine totalled about 50 lb. I used bricks, John Hamer used a sewing machine. Leave it until next day to remove the glass plates and cellophane. The latter peels off easily.

Try not to flex the laminate at this stage and do not separate the two halves. The edges of the wax foundation should be discernible through the translucent laminate. Use a hacksaw to cut off the excess at the foundation edges, such as to reveal all the foundation edges. The separation comes later on in the last stage of the press assembly.

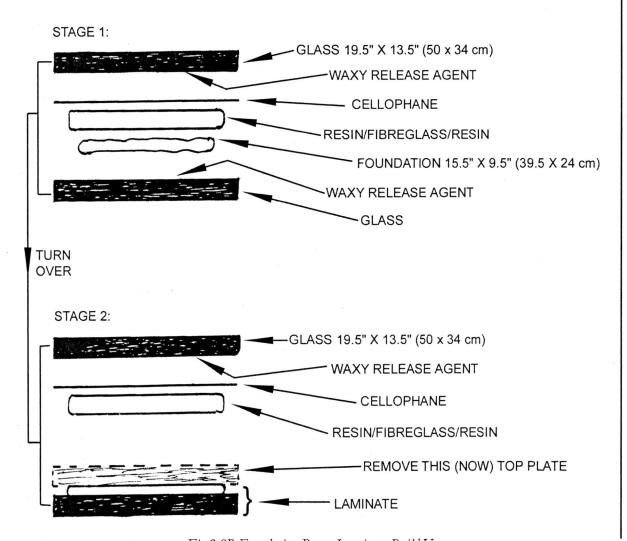

Fig 2.8B Foundation Press: Laminate Build Up

The Frame

The frame of the press includes two boards of 0.75 inch (20mm) thick external grade plywood. This absorbs very little water, and is unlikely to warp. The top board is 15.5 x 9.5 inches (394 x 242mm), the same size as the foundation. The bottom board is 16.5 x 10.5 inches (420 x 267mm) but its edge is cut at an angle (see fig 2.8C) all round so that timber fences glued on, on all sides, will form a tray. Use epoxy resin for this. It is waterproof. The choice of hinge and fixing method shown in fig 2.8D is the only way I could achieve satisfactory bending and opening operation. The fulcrum of the hinges should ideally coincide with the foundation plane. The handle is most usefully situated near the front, remote from the hinges.

Having made the wooden parts of the press and fixed the hinges (figs 2.8D and E) firmly and finally to your satisfaction, then the laminate can be installed. Prepare the inner faces of the press and both sides of the laminate by removing protruberances and roughing with coarse grade glass paper, as a key for the epoxy resin. With the laminate in place before fixing, and the top closed, there must not only be no gaps but the top should rest with a common pressure all over. This needs checking carefully at this stage. Try closing it upon a piece of paper held in different positions. See if the paper can be pulled away.

Only epoxy resin will withstand the water treatment that the press will encounter in use. 300g packs of Araldite® can be obtained from branches of Buck and Hickman. Avoid quick-setting versions of epoxy. Locate the laminate in the middle of the baseboard by bordering it with short, thin nails that won't interfere with the top when closed. The nails can be pulled out afterwards. Then coat the mating surfaces evenly with epoxy resin and close down. Weight the top down and leave overnight to set and harden. Next day the mating faces may be separated. The wax foundation is removed, leaving its imprint in the polyester resin. The mating surfaces of the resin will be used to imprint the pattern as the wax cools. A little heat may be needed to soften the foundation. As mentioned earlier, this sort of device is best made in the garage, or in

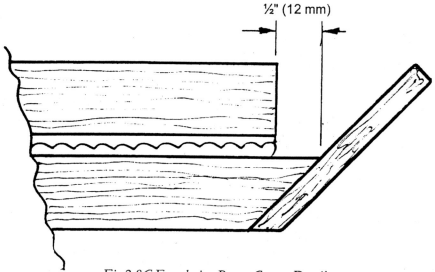

½" (12 mm)

Fig 2.8C Foundation Press: Corner Detail

the potting shed, not in the kitchen. Do it where you can later escape from the strong smell of the polyester resin. Any wax remaining on the fibreglass can be removed with a jet of boiling water.

Usage

This is a wet process, and some detergent must be added to the water to enable reasonable release of newly pressed foundation. Any wax containing unknown proportions of propolis is unsuitable for making into foundation by this process as it will stick to the plates. Set it aside for other purposes. Use good quality wax, that is, wax containing as little propolis as possible.

Sit the press in a wide water tray. I use a plastic tray obtained from a gardening supplier, 21 inches (530mm) square. This will contain the water (a thimbleful of domestic detergent to each two gallons (9L) of water will be necessary) with which the embossing faces must be wetted before each pressing. Then tip the surplus water away. Better still support it above the water tray on boards or a light frame, so that it is clear of the water when you apply the hot wax.

Set the press down horizontally, over the water. Take a jug of about 10 oz (280ml) of molten wax and, holding the press top open pour all of it steadily onto the base, directing the flow in a circular movement, so to avoid concentrating upon one spot. Close the press and hold the top down for a few seconds. Don't press hard. Leave it there while you lift the whole press up and pour the surplus wax out of the tray corner, back into the melting pot. At least one minute should elapse before the top can be lifted off. I usually score all around the edges with blunt knife to enable the new product to be peeled away. Any surplus wax that has set around

Fig 2.8D Foundation Press. Back of a Press: One Way of Fitting the Hinges
(which I found the most satisfactory)

the tray edges can be easily peeled off. Wet the ttray again in the water bath with the water/detergent mixture before pressing the next sheet of foundation. A large bucket of water with a handy saucepan, kept nearby, and also a siphon tube, are essential accessories, in order to drain and refresh the water tray.

If release is difficult, try some of the following:
1) Try not pressing down so tightly.
2) Pour cooler wax.
3) Leave it longer before pulling open.
4) Pour cold water onto the foundation if it is stuck to one face.
5) Look for factors that you can vary: temperature, timing, proportions of detergent, etc.

Sizing

A rectangular template to help cut exactly to the final foundation dimensions, is a necessary, final part of the process. Any sheet material will do. I use 1mm sheet steel, but in lesser order of preference, aluminium, plywood or hardboard will suffice.

Fig 2.8E Foundation Press. Back of a Press: Another Way of Fitting the Hinges

Frame Conversion

Sometimes a keeper wishes to convert from National to Commercial design hives. The transition frame shown here enables the change to be fulfilled. Several might be needed for a going colony during the active season, and the frames will need to stay in the hive for at least a season.

These frames may be constructed, as shown (fig 2.9). A Commercial deep/brood frame, used as a template, will give the dimensions needed. The metal ends of the National, inner, frames woll not be needed in the Commercial hive.

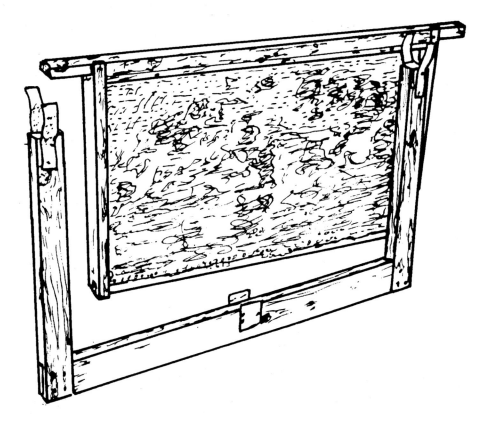

Fig 2.9 An easily made conversion frame enables National frames to fit into a commercial box.

Handling: Veils, Gloves, Smokers Bees and Hives

Veils

The best veils to be had are those which can give immediate access to the face by a zip at neck level, and are integrated with the jacket down to the waist and wrists. During very extensive veil usage I've had most of the elastic and some of the stitching replaced and even had one reveiled (mesh and zip were replaced). I like to have a long sleeved pullover under the veil jacket and pull on an additional, old pair of trousers over the ones I'm wearing. These give some needed extra protection from stings to the arms and legs, but one does get more overheated in it on a hot summer's day. This gear is finished off with Derry boots, or similar. These are one better than Wellingtons because they have pull cords around the tops to close off the bee access. Beginners will feel more confident in full bee protection gear, but as they become more experienced, and if their bees are normally docile they may choose not to don all of this bee armour on every occasion. Nevertheless it is wise to learn how to use it and have it with you for that rare belligerent occasion.

Leather Gloves

Beekeepers' leather gloves are given a tough job. They get caked with propolis and suffer hard usage when yanking this, hefting hives, lighting smokers, lifting rough bricks and worst of all, handling gummy frames. It is surprising that they last very long. And there is little or no advice as to looking after them.

I soaked one of a pair overnight in cold water with washing soda. This enabled me to scrub and scrape off some of the adhering lumps of propolis, but when dry, the glove had shrunk so much that it was no longer recognisable as belonging to the other one. It was also so shrivelled and hard that I couldn't begin to pull it onto my hand.

I remembered a letter published in 'BeeCraft', and unearthed it when looking for something else. It was January 1996. I tried its message, that is, to rub in some medicated paraffin, available from any chemist. I almost soaked it. It took a day or two of occasional manipulation to soften the leather, and I managed to wriggle my hand back into it. Ultimately it became as supple as new, albeit not the original colour, but who will worry about that?

Smokers

Most beekeepers use smokers automatically every time they open a hive. I look upon this as a bad habit and I find that smoking is rarely necessary. Following two years of re-queening and nucleus creation, all from those colonies with the very best non-aggressive history, I found I hardly ever needed a smoker. A vast improvement. Eventually I lost all my colonies and had to start again with whatever bees I could get. I now use a smoker only when I have to. Try to inspect a hive fully without smoke. Make a note of the difference. I must admit however, that smoke can be useful to clear the box tops when reassembling a hive, although I manage without, and squash very few bees.

A smoker can be lit at the first attempt every time using the following method. Floppy corrugated cardboard is rolled up and cut to fit the firebox is used. The essential detail is to leave a half inch (120mm) diameter hole up through the middle to act as a flue. This makes all the difference. Roll it round a finger sized rod. The outer turn is fixed with an elastic band or Sellotape®. It is lit at the bottom and inserted into the fire box. A few slow puffs, and it fires up every time. I use this cardboard only for lighting as it tars up the smoker more than other fuels. Partly dried grass, or sisal string or rotten wood are better fuels to use once the smoke is alight.

Handling Bees

The experienced beekeeper has seen the wildest colonies of bees, so vicious that they prompt even him to prepare a certain amount of courage and aforethought to do anything at all with them. This fortunately, doesn't occur too often. He has also seen colonies so docile that he needs neither a veil nor a shirt.

Most times that the bees have to be manipulated their behaviour tends to docility, but a small unpredictability prevails due to weather, time of year, and the foraging conditions of the day. But we may attribute to each hive a general level of temperament that we may recall from its history. Records of mood then, can be quite useful.

Fig 3.0A To light a smoker, leave a flue hole in the middle

Thus the experienced beekeeper can estimate the temperament of a hive when preparing to dismantle it for an inspection, and adjust his protective clothing to suit. Reasonable tolerance of bees to the beekeeper is normal, but the beekeeper develops an awareness of any change. I often start a manipulation with one glove on, and soon make a decision to either take it off or to don the other. After a couple of years I developed a reasonable tolerance to bee stings. I expect the odd couple of stings when inspecting my hives, but am convinced of the old wives tale that the stings prevent my arthritis.

Dealing with a vicious colony

A strong colony will occasionally not tolerate its hive being dismantled. Every bee available, it would seem, goes on the attack. A case will occur when even the clearance of undergrowth back from the hive close vicinity will invoke an angry onslaught. These occasions are rare, or they should be. However, the inured beeman should anticipate this if possible, and be ready for it even if it means a tactical withdrawal until another day, when they have calmed down.

Each time you inspect the brood combs, record a figure for docility, another for nervousness and also for following. Use your own form of coding. Don't count the number of stings, indices are more relevant and take less space. The rating should be logarithmic, e.g. 1 sting, 3; 10 stings, 30; etc. A keeper like myself with 10 hives has far better opportunities to select for docility from an array of these temperament observations than a keeper with only one or two hives.

Fig 3.0B Lighting the roll - it fires up every time

If a colony takes a hostile attitude throughout the season then a long term decision must be made. Requeening is the ideal answer. Occasionally a quick decision has to be made. The standard answer for this is to move the hive to a more isolated site, and to a spot at least three miles (5 Km) from its present apiary.

When being attacked by the bees which are trying to sting, it's no good running. They can fly faster. Swishing them away is to be avoided because this, and other fast movements, cause them to release alarm pheromone if they are not already doing so, summoning more bees into the conflict. This action causes a cloud of alarm scent to which they react with no delay. The best strategy is to just keep walking, preferably upwind, ideally under trees or bushes in order to leave this invisible cloud behind. If they then remain unappeased, then the best resort is to get back into the car or back indoors, and return later when they've calmed down.

Longer term improvements are effectively accomplished by selection. The occasions are when combining colonies or requeening. Make sure

1) you don't remove the wrong queen.
2) when prompting a self queening by inserting a frame containing eggs into a queenless colony. Be fussy which hive the eggs come from.
3) when queen rearing, a fickle operation, but more productive, obtain the young larvae from the right colony.

Moving a hive

When flying is in progress is not the ideal time to move a hive. You should wait until flying has stopped and all the bees are inside. Even then, unless it is cold, there is usually a bunch of them still clustered around the entrance.

There is a way to coax these ones to retreat inside too. All you need is a watering can with a finely perforated rose. Just water the front of the hive, bees and all. They think that its raining and disappear into the interior. You then stuff the entrance with a piece of polyfoam, and strap up the hive and it is ready to move.

Petroleum Jelly

Few beekeepers are aware of the useful applications of petroleum jelly. Bees are reluctant or unable to attach wax or propolis to surfaces of wood or any other materials that have been smeared with petroleum jelly. The peripheral faces of queen excluders thus smeared are easy to detach, such an advantage with the zinc and plastic versions. Try smearing the mating faces with petroleum jelly. It will come away much more easily as it discourages these mating faces getting propolised. This prevents the excluder getting stuck to the top of the brood box so tightly that it can get damaged in the tugging of just pulling it off.

I found that two removable, wooden cover strips that sit on the top of my pollen trap were regularly comb-braced to the bottoms of the frames above, and stayed there with them when I lifted the box off. When I cleaned them up and smeared on some petroleum jelly, the bees didn't do it any more.

A further aid to those inclined to the show benches with a comb of sealed honey is to smear those parts of a frame to which burr comb is to be discouraged. Thus a neatly delineated comb architecture can be expected.

Whether to Feed...

Having surveyed the problems specific to individual feeders (chapter3.5), the additional oncosts and risks should also be taken into account, and balanced against the value of leaving some of the bees' own honey on the hive. This honey is not more than a quarter of the sales price when the production costs are analysed. And it is not lost anyway. It will still be there in the spring. The great value of overwintered honey stores is in its influence on early spring population build up.

It could well be argued that the costs of sugar syrup feeding are higher than the value of any honey left on the hive.

Even if the sugar is purchased cheaply the additional costs in the time it takes to buy it, of mixing it and of feeding it, cannot be left out of the calculation.

When feeding, a robbing risk is introduced. I've lost two colonies in recent years after feeding sugar syrup, both completely written off, and neither were those in which the problem was initiated. One was started by a glugging contact feeder, and the other an indifferent roof of doubtful origin that didn't fit. Feeding can encourage a colony to breed at a time of year when breeding is normally running down, which is counter-productive for a honey harvest..

The great benefit of leaving the bees' own honey on the hive is that with the 50 to 70 lb (23 to 32Kg) total stores, and any associated pollen on board, after going through winter, the bees are conditioned and equipped for a boost of activity the following spring. This conditioning is not understood. Nor have I seen any published description, but it does imbue into the hive occupants a latent provision to excel in the coming season. All you have to do is to leave a full super on the hive. A colleague in Croydon never feeds, unless it is a nucleus, and he has yields of 70lbs (32Kg) minimum and sometimes over a hundred lb (45Kg) of honey from each hive, where I've been struggling to get a 30 lb (13.5Kg) average. Further, his honey does better in local shows. Its not diluted with syrup.

Which brood box?

Among the many discussions one experiences between beekeepers, the advocates for a bigger brood box are sometimes encountered. They go for a bigger hive design. There are several options. They use the brood and a half style, or the deeper British National brood box that takes 14 x 12 inch (355 x 305mm) frames. Some just adopt the Commercial brood box, a much different frame, but this box is at least compatible with National supers, roofs, etc.

The British National Brood box was first designed to give enough space for the brood of a healthy indigenous colony. It fulfils this aim admirably to this day. What it doesn't do, is to house sufficient autumn stores, to encourage a bumper yield the following year.

The big problem with these big boxes ie Commercial and Langstroth, comes when you have to lift them. If reason has to prevail, the best all round plan is to use a National brood box which will house the brood, and to use a super to hold the extra honey needed to boost the winter stores.

Collecting Swarms

The only essential equipment needed is:-

a large cardboard box, about a cubic foot (30cm cube) big
a small block of wood to prop up the cardboard box (see fig 3.1A)
an old sheet or dust cover, and of course
a hive, ready somewhere, in which to house the swarm.

Sometimes also needed:-

A smoker may be required if the last of the bees are reluctant to move
Soft brush
Shoe box
Steps
Transport

The swarm is sometimes discovered halfway up a tree. If you can't reach it forget it and go back home. It has a good chance of surviving on its own. Often, a swarm is positioned around a post, or in an awkward cavity where you cannot get a box underneath. In this case they just have to be brushed out, into a pan or a shoe box and further dropped into, or beside, the big box, or maybe, directly into the ultimate hive itself.

Fig 3.1A A cardboard box on a sheet is ideal to collect a swarm

A swarm sometimes settles on a bush at chest height. Never more convenient. First of all spread the sheet out on the ground near the swarm; under it if you can. Then hold the box, right way up, underneath the swarm, half the cluster hanging into it if possible. Give the supporting branch a violent jerk in order to dislodge the bees. Most should drop straight into the box. Take it to the sheet and slowly turn it up-side-down and leave it in the centre. If there is no gap under the box to give the bees access, prop one side up a little with an odd bit of wood, to make such a gap. The bees like to climb up and into the base of the box where it is dark.

Most of the bees disturbed by your action and flying around should join the main body and be inside the box in 20 to 30 minutes, with a few clustered around the gap. If they all fly out again it may be because the queen wasn't amongst the bees in the box, or that they didn't like the box. In this case you might have to collect them all over again. Don't wait for every last one to go in. Just wrap the sheet over and around the box when most bees are in, and take it to a full sized hive. Having once suffered the indignity of dropping a generous swarm into a nucleus box and seeing it immediately abandon the totally insufficient space, I now always prepare a full National deep brood box.

Even when it is settled, apparently snugly, there is no certainty that the newly housed swarm will stay. One failure I saw incurred an overnight stay before a thankless departing the next day. Another successfully housed swarm took umbrage three days later, when I dusted all its members over with icing sugar as a Varroa check. They left behind just a few bees and a tiny amount of brood. A swarm is geared up to moving house, settling in, drawing foundation and getting eggs laid - general housekeeping to take advantage of the honey flow and build up to survive the winter. I learned it is best to leave them alone for a while to get on with this.

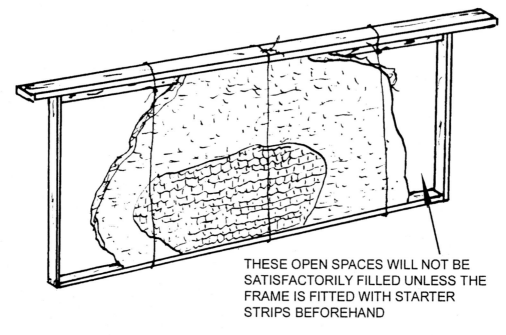

THESE OPEN SPACES WILL NOT BE SATISFACTORILY FILLED UNLESS THE FRAME IS FITTED WITH STARTER STRIPS BEFOREHAND

Fig 3.1B This problem comb, heavy with honey, will settle and buckle

I would assess that, of accessible swarms that can be dropped into a cardboard box, about four out of five can be hived successfully. Much depends upon the weather, the temperature and the attraction of your provided housing. This attraction can be enhanced if their new abode is first charged with some honey. But be aware of any introduced robbing risk.

Occasionally a swarm is found that has not moved on for a week or more, and that has built some comb in the open, quite unprotected from the weather. It has no chance of surviving the winter. This can be saved, but it takes a bit of preparation and about an hour or so to successfully install into a hive. This is how:-

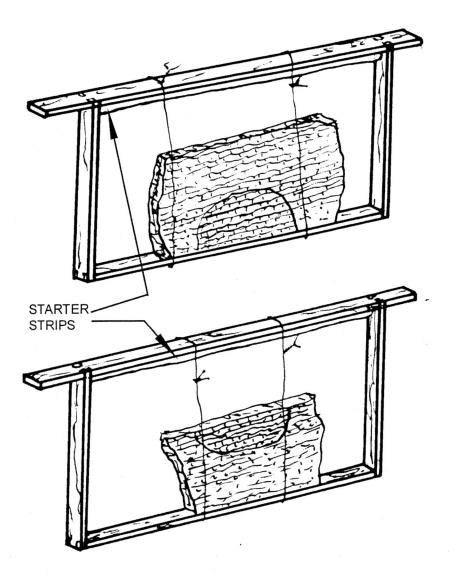

STARTER
STRIPS

Fig 3.1C A deep comb loaded with honey is too heavy and must be split

Prerequisites. -

A hive
Some empty frames, ideally fitted with starter strips
A couple of frames of foundation
Thin wire
Knife
Cutting pliers
Clean bucket with fitting lid for comb offcuts

Each piece of wild comb is cut away, with special care not to damage any more brood than is necessary. These combs must be individually cut to fit into a frame. Usually the height is cut in order to slide nicely into the space available. Regardless of the resulting comb height a flat base is needed to provide a stable seating upon the bottom bars. At least two loops of wire are then tied right over the top and bottom bars, and positioned and fastened, to hold the comb centrally in the frame (see fig 3.1C). Each comb is dealt with and placed in the hive, preferably with some of the bees, before the next is cut away.

Two problems that I have encountered which resulted in failure I describe here:-

1) Hived in the late autumn it failed to increase normally the following spring, in spite of feeding, and died out for the lack of pollen.

2) Hived on a warm morning in late June, the combs were warm and soft and heavily loaded with honey and brood, and were not sufficiently strong to retain their shape. As built naturally a comb is hanging, suspended from the top, it is in tension. A comb wired into a frame is not. It is in compression, and must be treated differently. They were heavy and settled badly and buckled, and adjacent combs rested against each other in several places, and the bees didn't take long to abscond. In hindsight I feel that, had I cut each of the heavier combs into two broad, horizontal bands, and fitted each part into its own frame, then the lower cells in each case wouldn't have suffered the same crushing effect.

Clearing Supers

Porter escapes are wonderful, because they work like magic. You lift the supers off, fit two escapes into the crown boards, set the supers back on and twenty four hours later nearly all the bees have gone down.

It is just that sometimes, perhaps more often than some like to admit, they don't work, there being just as many bees in the super as the day before. Or is it because you've not done it right? Either the bees just haven't gone down or they're getting back by another route as fast as they're going down. A few easy precautions and the escapes can be very reliable and effective:

Never leave them unchecked for more than forty eight hours, because bees are reluctant, very reluctant, to leave a comb face that has had brood in it, or otherwise just smells of brood. After two days bees that may be trapped start to show first signs of a rather sad decline. If you find this is happening you might have to brush the bees off each comb, thus to enable the supers to be freed of bees.

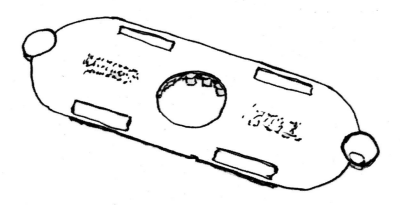

Fig 3.2 A Porter Escape. Fix it down with drawing pins

Too often the escape isn't seated properly. It can ease out of its slot in the clearer board if the fit is too tight, or it can be pushed up, or out of alignment, by burr comb underneath as you replace the clearer board. It pays well to be aware of these snags. Reliability is enhanced by fitting a drawing pin at each end of the escape to fix it down. Do make a point of taking away the porter escapes at the same time as the supers. The longer that they remain on the hive the more propolis they seem to collect. It saves such a lot of cleaning up.

The easiest way to remove propolis from Porter escapes is to immerse them in a strong solution of washing soda for a few hours. Leave them in it overnight. Put a bit of detergent in too. The propolis softens and is easy to remove with an old tooth brush. If you like them looking clean, the smeary remains of the propolis can be wiped off, using a rag dipped in a little with methylated spirit.

The Stand-By Escape

When take-off time comes and the supers are heavy, there is a way to move them once only, rather than twice. In correspondence with Dave Dawson, an ex-Surrey beekeeper, now bee farming in Canada, he explained how he did it.

Set up a floorboard near, but not in front of the hive, and place a clearer board upon it, ready fitted with porter escapes. Then lift the supers off the hive and onto the stand-by clearer. Put a flat board and a roof on the top. Make good the top of the hive, restoring its original roof, and leave the clearing to the bees. They all clear from the stand-by stack and go into their own hive. Thus you've only moved the supers once.

Fig 3.2B Hives: Preaparation for stand-by clearing

Removing Old Combs

Some of the brood box combs should be replaced each year as a rolling, long term, good beekeeping policy. This is a basic operation to discourage bee diseases, and should be part of the annual hive maintenance plan.

August

During a brood inspection.

Remove any combs in obviously bad condition e.g. those badly soiled by mice or mould.

Make a note of which combs:-

1) contain brood at any stage
2) need replacement; blackened with extensive brood
rearing, mouldy or distorted.

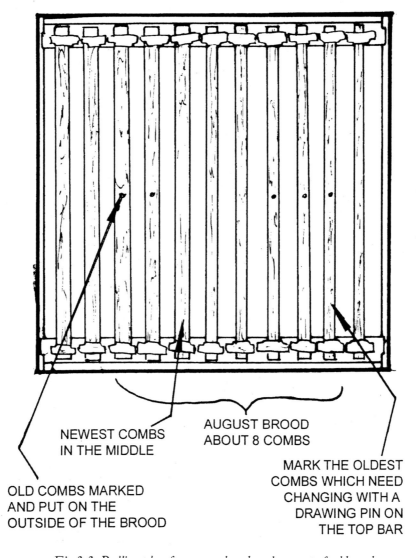

NEWEST COMBS
IN THE MIDDLE

AUGUST BROOD
ABOUT 8 COMBS

OLD COMBS MARKED
AND PUT ON THE
OUTSIDE OF THE BROOD

MARK THE OLDEST
COMBS WHICH NEED
CHANGING WITH A
DRAWING PIN ON
THE TOP BAR

Fig 3.3 Rolling plan for removal and replacement of old combs

Mark the worst 75%, approximately, of the brood box combs.   Adjust this proportion according to the urgency with which the brood needs a clean up. I use a red drawing pin pushed into the centre of the top bar. Remember that not all the marked combs will necessarily be removed next year. Rearrange the occupied brood combs by placing those not marked roughly in the centre between the marked ones. Ensure that the combs housing brood stay together. Leave the other combs in their original, relative order. The odd frame or two will survive the spring with a red drawing pin from last year. Add this year's pin to make two, and place these double marked combs on the outside of those with only one mark.

The Following March

The brood will have reduced to about two combs.

In the earliest suitable weather, take out those marked combs that do not contain brood, but leave most of the stored pollen where it is, within the hive. Move the other frames together. Make good with drawn comb or foundation placed on the outsides. The aim should be to replace 20 to 30% of the brood combs each year. I even note on my record cards how many combs I have salvaged so that I can adjust to an overall average next year.

The Comb Change

This is to be recommended when a hive has been neglected to the extent that, at best, the combs are blackened by prolonged brood rearing, but the combs may also be misshapen and mouldy, and the frames broken. All this, justifies replacing all the combs. This can only be done in the spring, during colony build-up, and then only if the queen is laying reasonably well. All the pollen in store is lost, and the colony will need to build a lot of comb. This will significantly reduce the honey yield for that year.

A new, or cleaned up, brood box is set up on top of the old one. It will have frames of foundation in it, and if possible, one or two of drawn comb. The queen is encouraged to lay in it by either of two ways.

1) Restrict her laying space in the old box by removing all the combs not containing brood and confining the remaining combs with divider boards. These are made of old frames that are clad on one or both sides with thin plywood. If she is a prolific queen she will soon run out of laying space and continue by laying in the box above. When she does, this will be the time to install the queen excluder between the two boxes, ensuring that the queen remains in the top box. Twenty one days from this time all the worker brood down below should have emerged then the old brood box and all the frames in it can be taken away.

2) Transfer one or preferably two combs from the old box, each ideally fully loaded with brood, and the queen herself, up into the newly installed box and flanked either side with drawn comb or foundation. Trap her there with a queen excluder so that she soon has no alternative than to start laying her eggs in the new frames. Then these two old combs can be transferred back to the old box below. It will then take another twenty one days for all the worker brood in the lower box to emerge as adult bees. During this time an upper entrance may be installed, between the two brood boxes and above the queen excluder. The lower entrance can then be blocked. When all the worker brood has emerged from the old box it can be removed complete, and all its contents salvaged and box and frames cleaned up.

The Upper Entrance

Some beekeepers use a high level, top of the brood box, entrance (fig 3.4). This is based upon the argument that bees returning with nectar have a shorter climb to take it up to the supers than from the conventional, low level entrance, thus enabling a quicker turnaround for the foragers. In this case the upper entrance goes under the queen excluder. When doing this it is best to use a thin, zinc or plastic excluder, so to avoid introducing yet more space between the brood and super boxes. When overwintering with an upper entrance fitted, it may be necessary to have an empty box on top, otherwise the roof won't sit down properly.

The Partial Comb Change

In a desperate case of bee disease or comb in a bad state, (I had a situation once in which three combs were hopelessly joined together by an array of brace comb), a compromise in the form of a partial comb change may be made. Half the combs containing brood, say three out of six are placed between divider boards in a temporarily installed brood box, and placed under the existing one, and with a queen excluder in between. If one also leaves them some of their pollen, then the colony has a better chance to build up and secure a reasonable crop of honey. The queen must be left in the existing brood box, above the queen excluder.

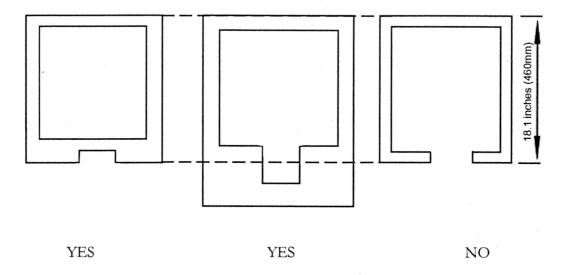

YES   YES   NO

Fig 3.4: The Upper Entrance, cut from 8mm plywood

Feeders

Bucket (rapid) Feeders

The bucket types in which the bees have to get up and over to get down to the syrup surface all have to limit the surface area accessible to the bees so that they don't get overwhelmed, and drown. These include the popular round, 'rapid' feeders, and the Miller, Ashforth and Brother Adam feeders. Any plastic or metal pot or dish can be used if some of the ultra-light, expanded polystyrene chips, used widely in packaging, are sprinkled on so as to cover the liquid surface. The pot, dish or tray is set under the roof with a spacer, if needed. The bees push under these chips and get at the syrup easily, and always have a foothold. This works wonderfully, they clean the dish quite dry. I've sometimes noticed that the bees' energy seems to be flagging in taking the syrup down. If it is left on the hive the stamina seems to worsen by the day. In this case the feed is best taken off.

A drawback of this sort of feeder is that if one bee, infected by nosema, drowns and becomes immersed, then the many thousands of spores infect the syrup and can be passed quickly through the whole hive.

Contact Feeders

In these feeders, the syrup is poured into a bucket or glass jar, and a lid, containing an aperture, skinned across with a fine mesh, or is finely perforated, is snapped or screwed on. You can make one yourself out of a screw-top jar. The whole is then upturned and set up, over a feed hole in the crown board. The bees take down the syrup from underneath and cannot get engulfed. It works well, but there are three potential problems:

1) When the feeder is turned over some spillage drips out. To avoid trouble caused by leaving spilt sugar in the apiary, do the upturning over a clean bucket that you have a lid for. Furthermore, it pays to fill it up, to reduce this effect to a minimum. The syrup is not compressible. Filling the feeder reduces the compressible, elastic, trapped air, reducing spillage.

2) Contact feeders can sometimes glug out and start emptying by themselves. This has happened to me. Once, with a weak colony it started a robbing phase. It is worth while when installing this type of feeder, to use a spirit level to ensure it is perfectly level.

3) As the overnight cooler temperature approaches, the air in the contact feeder contracts and allows in more air. The following morning the air expands again and causes the syrup to drip and can flood part of the hive.

I lost a colony over a glugging feeder. It started a robbing phase that was only stopped by interchanging the victim hive with that of a much stronger colony. The victim survived, and I thought I'd solved the problem. The strong one showed signs of being robbed the following spring and died out as a result. The lesson to be learnt from this is to move the victim right away (over three miles), and vacate the robbed spot for a whole season.

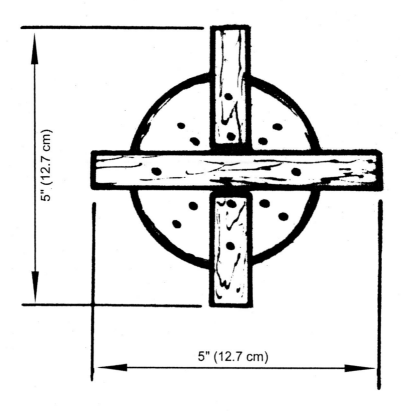

5" (12.7 cm)

5" (12.7 cm)

*Fig 3.5A Water Feeders: Coffee jar lid modification: fit three strips to form a cross.
Drill small holes between to feed water out slowly.*

So, the beekeeper needs to be aware of the properties, the pros and cons of each, to choose between these two types of feeder. I avoid giving syrup with these feeders unless there is no other way. I have adopted the practice of leaving enough honey on each hive to keep them going through the winter. The best way of all to feed, as discussed in chapter 3.0, page 75, is to leave sealed honey on the hive, a whole super full, in which case you'll not need to feed at all.

Water Feeder

Bees need water. If there is no pond, stream or ready source of water nearby, caring hive owners who provide water feeders nearby will certainly get the chance to see the bees taking the water.

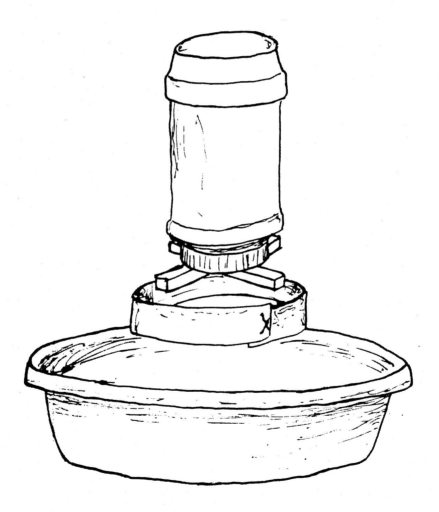

Fig 3.5B Feeders: A home made bowl and jar water feeder.

A water feeder can easily be made using a plastic washing up bowl as the basis. It should be pierced with small holes through the sides, an inch (2.5cm) up from the bottom at six points round the sides. This prevents the bowl from overfilling during above average rainfall.

A large coffee jar is used as a water reservoir. The rarer 12 oz (350g) size is ideal, but an 8 oz (250g) jar will do. The screw-on lid may be adapted to provide spaceers for the water to escape in the following way (fig 3.5A):

Three small strips of wood or plastic are attached to the lid top face. Each is fixed with two small wood screws from inside the lid. Eight holes each 0.12 inch (3mm) diameter; (no bigger, or the bees will get in and be unable to get out), are drilled through the lid, the jar is filled with water and the lid screwed on. Finger tight is quite adequate. The jar is turned over and set up-side-down into the bowl. It is recommended to bring the jar indoors during the winter to protect it from frost.

A strip of perforated zinc about 2 inches (5cm) wide can be cut, and joined at the ends with wire to form a circle of about 5.5 inches (14cm) in diameter. Sit this in the bowl around the jar and use it as a barrier to hold back some peat, dried grass, or other suitable fibrous material outside it. This material will retain the water and provide a surface for the bees to land on, grip onto, and will prevent the risk of drowning.

Records

Even if you have only one hive of bees, some sort of a system of keeping records of what you find in it and what you have done, is a very useful reference.

The more hives you deal with, the more involved the manipulations and researches, so the more indispensable are your dated notes. Further, they are more useful the better order they are in and if you can find what you are looking for.

The notebook is good, perhaps the best way to start, but it becomes inconvenient later, when seeking what you wrote. It has a useful role however, as a complement to formatted entries. Always remember to enter the date.

Tabulated data, record cards, or other loose-leaf systems are far better for looking up. This is because they help you to record salient, hard facts and to bypass most of the irrelevant.

Start with a modest system aimed to record say, a year's work. After this you will have a better idea of what is needed.

A card for each hive is widely practised and a system I adopted as the most useful from 15 years of beekeeping. I show the one I use (fig 3.6A overleaf and Appendix I). Better equipped photocopy shops can copy your masters on to thicker, 200 gsm, paper.

From October or thereabouts, from when the honeybees can be left undisturbed, heading 'A' can be filled in with fact, picked out from the year's notes, the facts that contribute to decisions and plans for action the following year. These headings are referred to when selecting colonies for requeening or from which to breed.

If, like me, you are a persistant and purposeful experimenter, then you need to get into the records habit more than most. When making observations, writing articles for beekeeping magazines, or a book like this one, good record keeping provides a solid basis for decision making and recommending successful beekeeping practices to others.

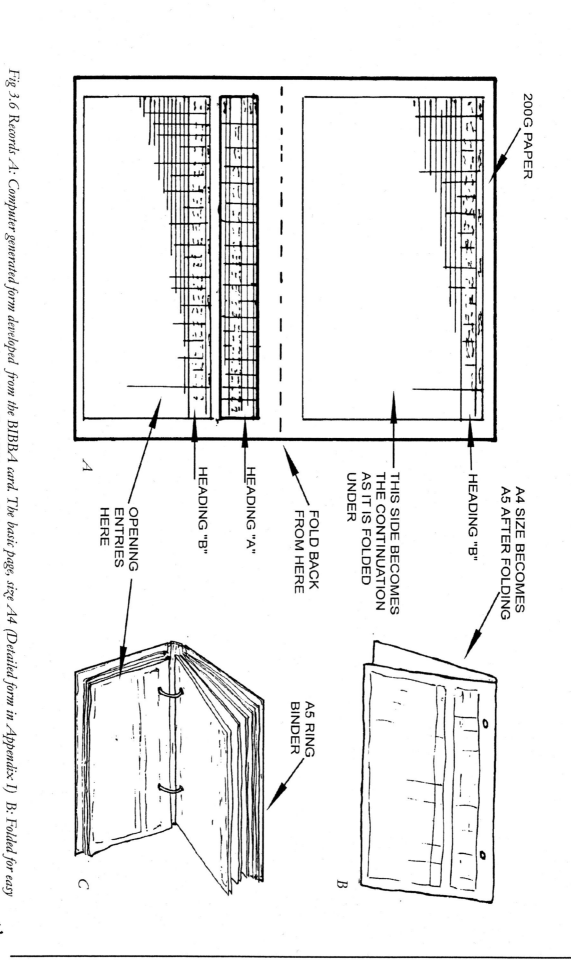

200G PAPER

A4 PAPER

A4 SIZE BECOMES
A5 AFTER FOLDING

HEADING "B"

THIS SIDE BECOMES
THE CONTINUATION
AS IT IS FOLDED
UNDER

FOLD BACK
FROM HERE

HEADING "A"

HEADING "B"

OPENING
ENTRIES
HERE

A

A5 RING
BINDER

B

C

Fig 3.6 Records A: Computer generated form developed from the BIBBA card. The basic page, size A4 (Detailed form in Appendix I) B: Folded for easy use at the Apiary C: All hive records kept in an A5 ring binder

Care of Comb

Wax Moth

Drawn comb can be useful in beekeeping operations and is thus a valuable asset. However, comb out of the hive and in store, will ultimately be located by the sinister wax moth. The moth lays its eggs in the covert corners of the frame, in total darkness, and later, the emerging larvae eat, and make tunnels, through the comb, and reduce it to a revolting, webby and frassy mess. It becomes quite unusable. Left unattended, more moths will emerge and wreak yet further damage.

To protect this valuable resource the owner should consider at least one of the following defences.

1) A sealed store. A cupboard with no gaps? How do you ensure that the comb is not infected before it goes into the store?
2) Render most of the comb into wax blocks, in which form it is safe, and make foundation from it when needed.
3) Sprinkle paradichlorobenzine (PDB) crystals into the boxes of comb. This practice is widely used, usually in conjunction with newspaper separation of the boxes. This deters wax moth entry.
4) Inspections: Each 2 months in summer. Each 4 months in winter. Remove any visible moth larvae.
5) Set a bait of old combs that are condemned for ultimate rendering. These must be inspected for moth presence regularly.
6) Leave more of the combs on the hives. The bees have a protective vigilance.
7) An overnight stay in a freezer will kill all living moths.

PDB crystals are effective but evaporate in the long term, but the vapour is retained by the frames and in the wax for a long time. Combs treated with PDB should normally be aired before use. During an airing they are accessible to the moths again. Few bee people who put combs aside for future use estimate how long the combs they are saving are going to stay there.

Many beekeepers practice newspaper separation. This involves a stack of beehive boxes of stored comb, in which each box is set upon the one below, but with a sheet of newspaper in between. Two thicknesses give better protection, or I sometimes use squares of redundant lino or wallpaper. The philosophy is that any laying moths will be restricted to lay her eggs in only one compartment. But it must be remembered, this system, and the use of PDB crystals, only buys time.

I have always advocated an ongoing vigilance, in the form of inspections. Each comb is visually checked at least twice a year, that is, in late autumn and early spring. Skill in spotting even the earliest infections is quickly acquired. Evidence of slight disturbance around the wedges, and slots in the side bars, is easily seen. Evidence sometimes occurs in the middle of the comb. Look for traces of web. The necessary perusal takes little more time than picking up the comb and putting it down. Sometimes a judicious local search can locate the offending maggot.

However, I had to change my frequency of inspection in 1996 when I found so many early traces. Reacting quickly to the unusually high moth activity, I was inspecting all my stored comb every three or four weeks. That season followed the consolidation of varroa in my area. I attributed the moth infestation to the higher degree of unoccupied comb still around. Anyway, I solared most of my comb and boxed up the remainder with PDB crystals. Thereafter I changed my previous practice to storing only enough drawn comb to fulfil my presicted needs for the following season.

Once discovered the infested frame is booked for an overnight stay in the freezer. This kills the moth in all its stages. The problem here is that when the comb is put back with the others, and evidence of moth movements are spotted in later inspections one cannot determine if it is a new or previously treated infection.

One day when fitting foundation to a batch of used frames, I found that every other frame housed a little wiggly grub. I couldn't rely on finding all of them, and settled for slapping the empty frame, less the wedge, down on the bench. This dislodged them quickly. One or two frames got cracked in the process though, and needed gluing up. An overnight stint in a freezer is a more reliable cure.

A Frame Clamp

This has been found invaluable for the times when frames of foundation and comb are transported in the car. Any number of frames, with or without metal ends, and within their boxes, can be held securely. It can easily be made from one piece of plywood and elasticated luggage hooks as shown in fig 3.7B, and in use in 3.7A.

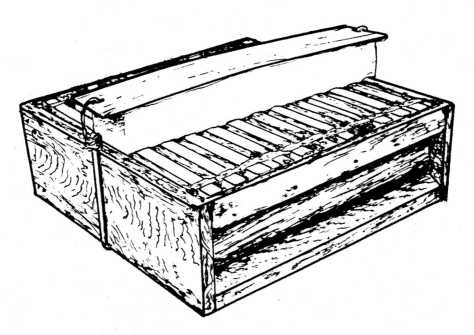

Fig 3.7A Frame clamp fitted

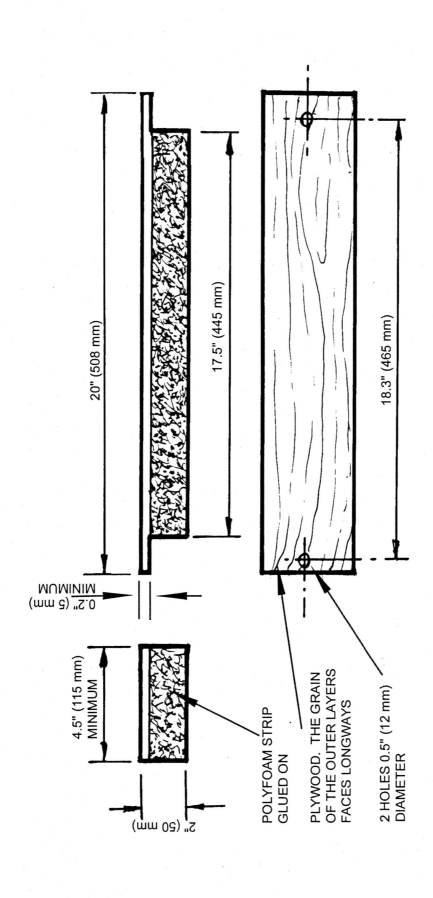

20" (508 mm)

17.5" (445 mm)

18.3" (465 mm)

0.2" (5 mm)
MINIMUM

4.5" (115 mm)
MINIMUM

2" (50 mm)

POLYFOAM STRIP
GLUED ON

PLYWOOD. THE GRAIN
OF THE OUTER LAYERS
FACES LONGWAYS

2 HOLES 0.5" (12 mm)
DIAMETER

Fig 3.7B Frame clamp

Queens

Care, respect and recording (chapter 3.6) of your queens' presence and characteristics are imperative for two general reasons:

1)   If she goes missing, or dies, or just stops laying, you need to know immediately as her colony is in trouble and may start on a steady demise. The beekeeper himself may inadvertently causes the trouble. With vigilance he can help to avoid it, and maybe restore stability if things go wrong.

2)   In her lies the assets and liabilities of the strain. These qualities are assessed by observations of her offspring; of her workers in the main, but even her young queens and sons (drones). Here lies one of the values of your recorded notes.

A long list of strain criteria may be drawn up. Opinions of old head these lists (see chapter 6.1) with 'aggression', i.e. readiness to sting, but propensity to swarm and disease resistance are usually highly placed on these lists.

Finding Queens

Most worthwhile brood operations start with 'first find the queen'. The quickest way to find her is by the sheer experience of finding queens. Looking for her. So, whenever you have brood frames out, always keep an eye out for the queen. If you are a beginner this makes good practice.

Rather than searching by looking at each bee, cast the eyes around each comb of bees in an overall, sweeping style, seeking out a long abdomen. This is the main physical difference between a queen and each of a host of workers. Also a queen seems to have a gait all her own.

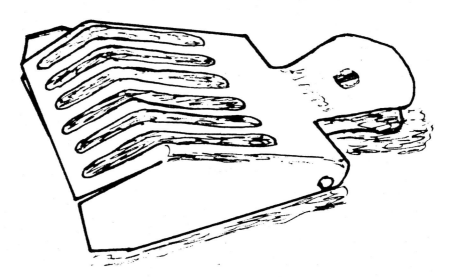

*Fig 3.8A Queen catcher clip. The best way to retain
the queen so that you know where she is.*

She moves around the comb in a more positive way than the workers. She keeps moving. This also helps to show her up.

Should you be unable to find your queen after all this, then look in the supers to check if she has penetrated or bypassed the original queen excluder and has started laying eggs there. Whenever you take off a queen excluder, always scan the underside in order to ensure that the queen is not there.

It is much easier to find the queen if the colony is small. e.g. early in the spring, or in a nucleus box. Thus, it follows that if you can choose when to carry out your planned exercise for which you need to find the queen, choose that time when the population is on the low side. It is only accumulated experience that helps me to find her most times. Practice in any work does improve one's skill. This is true for finding queens. One method that I sometimes resort to is to set each brood frame, after a thorough search, down into an empty brood box, keeping them in the same order, so that the queen can't do a crafty move onto it from a frame

Fig 3.8B Hair roller. An old favourite for caging the queen.

that I've yet to examine. Often, the old box needs taking away for a clean-up or a repair anyway. This method often facilitates a welcome opportunity to rehouse the brood into a better, cleaned up box.

Marking Queens

I don't mark queens, but I do clip them. I tried marking some queens with an ultra-violet responsive security marker. When looking for her during a later manipulation, I used a UV detective lamp to find her. It showed her up alright but I had to hold it so close to her that there was little practical advantage. It might work better if you can switch the lights off!

If all you want is to ensure her presence, then you only need to return her, on the comb she was found, back into the hive. If however, a manipulation is planned then she usually needs setting aside for a few minutes where she is safe and can be found.

Restraining the Queen

Once I've spotted her I isolate her. I used to put her, together with the frame I found her on, into an empty nucleus box, there to stay until I was reassembling the hive. This practice is now superseded. My preference is now for the queen clip catcher, a simple cage which holds the queen closely until I am finished with the hive manipulation, when I can set her down in the chosen part of the hive during reassembly.

I do not attach great value to queen marking. The queen's age can be determined with equal certainty from hive records, and clipping.

Clipping Queens

The great advantage of queen clipping is that one needs to inspect for signs of swarming only once a fortnight, instead of weekly. A further argument is that it is less disturbing to the whole hive. A detailed timing for queen clipping is adequately covered by Hooper (1976) .

Clipping entails the removing of about 1.5mm of the tips of both wings so that she is unable to fly out with a swarm. Some pick her up between finger and thumb. I heard of one quick fingered beekeeper who followed her with sharp nail scissors and clipped her while she was on the run. I find it convenient to hold her down on the comb face with one forefinger while I perform the snipping. It is important to avoid pressing the abdomen but to hold her down by the thorax; the middle section. This is much tougher. Don't cut too much off the front edge of the wing as it bears a blood vessel. Within the hive both wings lay back, one upon the other so you can usually clip both together. A pair of sharp nail scissors is best suited. Make sure that no queen's legs get in the way.

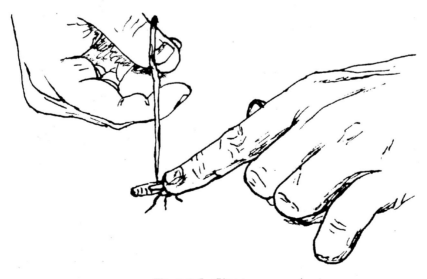

Fig 3.8C Clipping a queen's wings

You must only clip a queen that is laying satisfactorily. This is done ideally in about March, following her year of emergence.

Queen Rearing

Queen Rearing itself is covered in general beekeeping reference books and booklets available from BIBBA.

One of the problems encountered when rearing queens is when the incident queen gets through the excluder. When this happened to me I realised that the queen, in being separated by the excluder from all of her brood, is then desperate to get back to it. She will search and push when, in normal times there would be no need. It seemed that in her newly enhanced desire to be among her brood she scans the excluder seeking a way through. Of the assortment of excluders in my possession I found that I was using the least suitable for queen rearing. Each of the makers represented among my excluders sets a different spacing. This subtle detail was the downfall of my queen rearing efforts one year. So I set about measuring which excluders had the narrowest gaps.

The easiest way to measure the gaps accurately was to lay a twelve inch rule across the grid wires and count forty pitches. Note the dimension. It should be about 9.5 inches. Now divide this by forty. But this assumes that the wires used in each of the excluders are all of the same diameter. Measuring the spaces is not quite so easy. I found an engineer's taper pin. This allowed me to compare one space against any other.

Introducing Queens into a New Colony

A quick way to introduce a queen is to dab her with a little honey, not enough to drown her! When the workers encounter her all instincts are subordinated to collecting the honey.

I once saw several bees and wasps all side by side taking up honey from a piece of comb I had dropped. Mutual intolerance just disappeared.

Pests

Ants

In the summer ants' nests can be seen almost everywhere. If they find any source of sugar they can bring large numbers to take full advantage of their discovery, whether indoors or outside. This is by no means confined to summer months and, like bees, they can work just as effectively in daylight or darkness. Beehives, solar wax extractors, stacked boxes of sealed honey or even old combs are prone to invasion, by ants, once discovered. They can cause a bee colony to abscond.

The perfect answer is the oil tray. It stops the very worst of ant invasions within the hour. The basis is trays of oil (don't use old engine oil, it contains carcinogenic substances), or water, with a few drops of paraffin oil added. Ensure that the paraffin spreads and forms a thin skin across the surface of the water. Add a little detergent if you like. This will kill the ants. The most easily available trays are the aluminium foil food trays popularly used by Chinese and fast food takeaways. They are flimsy perhaps, but with care, they will do the job. First, check against a bright lamp that there are no pin holes in them.

Find, or cut, a piece of wood to sit in each tray and which will support wooden beams or a square of plywood clear and above the trays. Give the blocks two coats of polyurethane varnish. This prevents the blocks soaking up the oil and transferring it into the timbers of the hive or whatever else it supports.

If it is set up outside, there is little lost if rain gets into the trays because a little paraffin on top of the water is all that is needed. Plywood boards of 6 to 12 inches (15 to 30cm) square might be found useful if placed under each oil tray to give more stable, level, placement on rough ground.

Fig 3.9A Ant Barrier: foil tray, wooden block and oil.

Fig 3.9B Ant Barrier: set hives upon foil trays (on a bumble nest box)

Fig 3.9C Ant Barrier: oil trays give total immunity

I usually keep a few used screw-top lids around, from 1 lb (454g) honey jars. They may be slightly dented or scratched, but they are sometimes useful. My recent discovery is that they can be used as compact oil trays with a used plastic bottle top; 1 3/4" (43mm) dia. x 3/4" (19mm) high. I put metal weights in the bottle tops, otherwise they float. Although a fill of water works

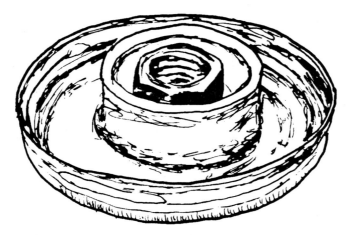

Fig 3.9D Tin lid: honey jar screw cap lid used as an oil tray. Weighted in the middle to stop the plastic bottle top floating.

well in the short term, oil of some kind is better as water evaporates and precipitates rust. If ants are known to be around this small tray should be checked visually each day. Ants can easily bridge the moat by filling it up one side with dead ants and debris.

Mice and Mouse Guards

To prevent harmful disturbance in winter, a beekeeper must protect his bees from mice. A beehive makes quite a cosy shelter for a mouse or two, away from the worst of the elements, with a larder for sustenance too. Such a resident mouse couldn't be better provided. Not such settling inquiline company for the bees though. You can buy ready made mouse guards which need fixing on in the autumn before the incidence of frost, and removing in the spring.

It can be quite convenient to have two sets of entrance blocks, one set for the summer, and one for the winter. This is because the winter blocks have the mouse guards built in. The winter entrance blocks are fairly easy to make, by making a permanent adaptation to a summer entrance block.

The mouse barrier added in the form of a row of 0.75 inch (20mm) nails, hammered into the entrance block, and equally spaced across the entrance gap. Use brass nails if you can as they don't rust. The spacing of 0.31 inch (8mm) can be accurately marked out with a piece of broken hacksaw blade, and a scriber. The blade must be a little shorter than the entrance gap width. A stout needle will suffice for a scriber. Sitting the hacksaw blade across the gap, the teeth can be used to estimate the nail spacings. Six teeth, or that number that gives the correct spacing, mark the place, then move along the blade and prick another hole, and so on. This will give regular spacing, and a straight line. It might help if holes are positioned with a fine drill before knocking in the nails. Then check with a steel rule, used as a straight edge, across the top of the nail heads to check that the nails don't protrude too far, and the entrance block can be pushed home (fig 3.9F).

Wasps

Come August and September when the wasp numbers maximise, they can constantly attempt to bypass the bee guards at the hive entrance. In an energetic flight pattern they seek a chance to enter the hive. The bees are normally quite capable of rebuffing these constant advances, but some wasps manage to achieve entry, the beekeeper often finds one or two robbing and dodging inside the hive. Rarely, the wasps can overcome the bees' defences and clean the hive out dry.

The keeper can help his bees by narrowing the entrance. Most of my entrance blocks house a three or four inch wide opening. I can usually find a more suitable, narrow entrance, say one inch wide, from my collection of entrance blocks, for when necessity calls for a tighter restriction. When robbing is obviously going on, a single bee width

Fig 3.9E Making a Mouse Guard.
Aim for 8 mm spacing. Point the holes
using a broken hacksaw blade.

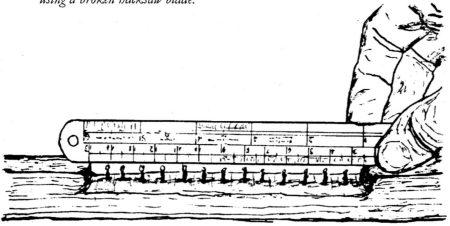

Fig 3.9F Check with a straight edge that none of the nails protrude

entrance is better, but the removal of the target hive to another site is an even more reliable remedy.

The wasp trap in the form of an old jam jar, can be resorted to. An inch of sweetened water in it will attract the wasps, but not the bees, and a drop of detergent in the potion will ensure that the wasps drown. Bait it with a little jam or marmalade; not honey. Ale is sometimes used, or a piece of meat. Polythene film is stretched across the top and fixed with an elastic band, and a hole is made in the middle of it just big enough for the wasps to get through. When there is a severe threat from wasps, I recommend fitting several of these traps, all near hive entrances where the wasps concentrate.

In the case of a hive or nucleus which is weak where wasps are going in with little or no opposition, the only practical resort is to move it, even temporarily, to another site. Commercial wasp traps are sometimes seen in the shops. They can be very effective, if expensive.

Fig 3.9G Wasp Traps: the well-known jam jar is cheapest.

Woodpeckers

Woodpeckers are rarely a problem, that is, until the frostiest of weather makes itself felt. If desperate for sustenance they are quite capable of chopping their way into a brood box, and usually leave evidence of having pecked at more than one hive face before breaking in. A successful intrusion means a quick and violent end to the bees. However, like all seasoned thieves the woodpecker carefully assesses the prospects of its escape route. Its power is in its wings, and the wings need a big sweep in order to ensure a swift departure. Entanglement would prevent escape.

Any lacy hangings surrounding a hive will discourage a woodpecker from considering an intrusion. Hang any webbing, curtaining, pea and bean netting or the like down from around the roof. I found some redundant greenhouse shading for my hives. Don't forget to leave the bees access to their entrance. However, sometimes woodpeckers get the taste for bees and these deterrents are inadequate. At these times a chicken wire cage is needed, spaced two inches all round so that the beekeeper can lift it off for access.

Wax Moths

For prevention of wax moth damage on stored comb see chapter 3.7.

When you open a hive which has an empty super or two you see just a few bees on every comb, not appearing to be doing anything in particular. There are even a few dotted around the super box walls and in the roof space. What are they doing up there? Why aren't they down near the brood where there are a score of jobs that need their labours? Those workers set about here and there up aloft and in the roof are probably on essential wax moth vigilance. They are as much on guard as those grouped at the entrance. They kill or repel the moth quickly. Unless stopped, the sinister intruder secretes eggs in covert corners, if they can, where the workers can't get access. From then on defensive opportunity is gone. I once saw a brood box heaving with wax moth larvae, and smothered with web. The brood was doomed long before the invasion advanced that far. It showed me the complete desecration of comb and brood, the tragic result, precipitated possibly by just one moth. I had inadvertently put the moth eggs there. Once the flying moth, or moths, gain unchallenged access to wax comb and lay eggs, the sad fate of the hive is set.

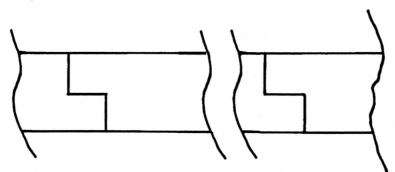

Fig 3.9H Moths: Section of a floorboard showing rebates

Some writers say 'crack the propolis and sit the crown board on some matchsticks' as spacers, to enhance ventilation. I feel that the propolis is there to seal off much of the moth access. Individual beekeepers are welcome to test both these theories. Maybe the different conditions in different areas affect susceptibility to wax moth invasion. Well kept records will determine what works for your bees.

Regard every frame that has been removed from a hive, for whatever reason, as possibly carrying wax moth eggs or larvae. Every other one has the odd moth larva or eggs hidden in it somewhere. This, in spite of the ongoing protective programme of the honeybees. If the combs have been sitting about elsewhere, the prospects of infestation are much worse. In a frame the favourite hiding place is behind the wedge, but the larvae may be found anywhere where there is wax. Unless a comb is old and booked for an early session in the solar wax extractor, the best way to buy time is an overnight sojourn in the freezer. This kills the moth in all its stages.

Furthermore, to prevent wax moth invasion newly acquired boxes of sealed honey should be extracted as soon as possible. If you have to wait several days before extracting, they're safer left on the hives until you are ready to extract. As moth activity is enhanced with temperature it is best to store combs in as cool a place as possible eg a shed or unheated garage. Set up the boxes of combs in mock hive form outdoors on a frosty night. This has the same effect as in a freezer.

Always store hive floor boards separately, preferably in a different shed or room from fitted foundation or drawn comb, unless they have first been baked in a solar panel (or spent 24 hours in a freezer). Floor boards are a perennial source of emerging moths. The larvae can hide the rebate joints (fig 3.9H), where they pupate and emerge later as moths when you're thinking of other things. I prefer a floorboard design based upon a one-piece exterior grade ply sheet.

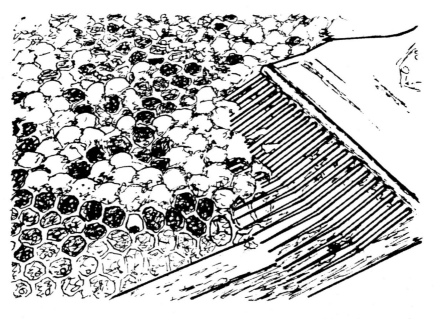

Fig 3.9J Drone capping fork: impale some sealed brood

Used frames in store, even empty ones, constitute a cosy haven for the larvae. I've found so many. Look for the webby traces that they leave in their wake. Acetic acid sterilisation of hives and combs is also very effective against wax moths and other nasties.

Pollen traps and Varroa screens are classic attractions for moths. For this reason I install these in the hive for the minimum time possible. Honeybees do carry out some in house prevention against wax moth invasion, but they are obviously at a disadvantage if they can't access the moths or their larvae. These temporary pedestal boxes do have inaccessible corners and niches and are thus eminently supplied with ideal housing where the moths settle and breed and are well protected from any adverse attention from the bees.

Varroa

It is necessary to make checks to ensure that the parasitic spider *Varroa jacobsoni* is not increasing in the hives faster than the beekeeper anticipates. Methods of monitoring such as natural mite drop and the uncapping of drone brood (figs 3.9J and K) may be used.

There is now a need to check regularly for signs of resistance to Apistan® and Bayvarol® if these treatments are being used. The National Bee Unit provides details of a simple test method that can be used by beekeepers.

There is a need to use the treatments Apistan® and Bayvarol® properly and according to the suppliers' instructions. Also to support the use of these treatments by alternation with a non-chemical, biotechnical method such as an open meshed floor in place of a normal floor board and to practice drone removal in the summer. A combination of these approaches can buy extra time before chemical treatments are again required.

Foul Brood Diseases

Foul brood disease is the beekeepers' (and bees') major frustration. Beekeepers might well be insured for foul brood, but each of us would rather avoid seeing our year's work inexorably destroyed.

The two foul broods can be outlined here:

European Foul Brood (EFB) is caused by the bacterium *Mellisococcus plutonius*. If spotted in the early stages this can often be treated with antibiotics by a bee inspector, and the colony saved.

American Foul Brood (AFB) is caused by the bacterium *Paenibacillus larvae subspecies larvae*. The colonies affected must be destroyed.

European Foul Brood (EFB)

Workers are known, and seen, to clear dead bees, larvae and pupae right out of the hive. In the case of EFB, however, the workers of a strong colony can and do remove dead larvae if the spread hasn't extended seriously enough to undermine the energy of the hive workforce, but the emptied cells remain and can further contaminate larvae or stores.

American Foul Brood (AFB)

In the case of AFB, an infected pupa turns into a sticky mess and the workers get little chance to clear it out. The worker would become contaminated in the attempt anyway. This, and the fact that, of the two reportable brood diseases, AFB makes very long-lived and tough, infectious spores is why, in AFB outbreaks, the MAFF (now DEFRA) insists that all the contents of the hive are invariably burnt.

It has been well reported that AFB spores can sometimes be found in honey from colonies not (yet) showing visible signs of the disease.

Apiary Hygiene

The beekeeper can generally help here by an annual replacement of a proportion of the brood combs with new foundation. My hives were once found with EFB, and subsequent to the incineration session, a reasoned deduction left no doubt that feeding with their own honey,

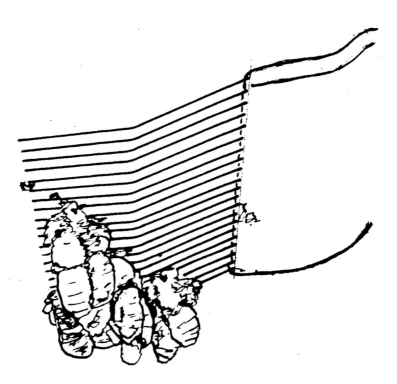

Fig 3.9K Drone brood lifted out: inspect the brood for mites

that by the way of a solar extractor, was the major vector in the malady spread.. Based upon this unhappy experience I resolved never to feed the bees with anything other than sugar syrup. I reject the now worn out adage that it is alright to feed with their own honey. It is tantamount to recycling the infection.

Further to this, it must be accepted that the beginning of an infection can start with just one bee; quite unseen. There are many ways that the beekeeper can inadvertantly help an infection to spread. Make a note of all the occasions in a year that you take a comb from one colony and put it in another, and deduce how many of these swaps could have been avoided.

Immerse your tools and used frames in boiling water: hive tools, queen catcher clips, smoker, porter escapes, metal ends etc. I carry my hive tools in a bucket of a solution of washing soda crystals, in the same way as my Regional Bee Inspector. He also uses disposable plastic gloves.

By far the best approach to avoid spreading infection is to act as though it is already in your hives. It might well often actually be there and you don't know. Assume that it is and adopt, as near as possible, in the field, a hygienic technique. Prevention is better than cure.

If you make your own foundation and aspire to make a sterile wax you will need to ensure a high minimum temperature in the melting plan. When making foundation I now use three separate sets of double saucepans. One for melting the lumps, a second to ensure a high temperature and the third, kept at a lower temperature for pouring onto the foundation press.

A temperature close to 100degC is readily attainable with a double saucepan with water in the lower pot. This will kill EFB infection. I do this when making foundation.

A higher temperature of 120degC is needed though, to deal effectively with AFB. This cannot be met by the use of the aforementioned double saucepan. It can be achieved by setting the wax pot directly upon a hot plate or electric ring. You may have to stir continuously to avoid damaging the wax. Don't do it on a flame heat as the wax is inflammable and you will risk causing a fire. Use a deep saucepan because the depth of wax is doubled by the wax froth that is involved. This process is not recommended for the hobbyist.

Considering that the first signs of foul brood infection may be so slight that they are unlikely to be recognised, the following good practice, as a reaction to any foul outbreak in your vicinity is suggested. It would be prudent to be more energetic than usual in replacing older brood combs for at least a couple of years, or in preference, until all your combs have been changed. Any wax rendered from these combs during this time would be used wisely for candle making, or other arts and crafts applications.

More information on honey bee foul brood is available from the National Bee Unit.

Extracting Honey

If, like most beekeepers, you're extracting your own honey, you will need an uncapping peg. This takes the weight of the comb and steadies the comb while you're doing your knifing act.

First get a new suitable plastic bowl at least 14 inches (355mm) diameter to accept the cappings, and keep it for this purpose alone. Then the three pieces of timber can be selected

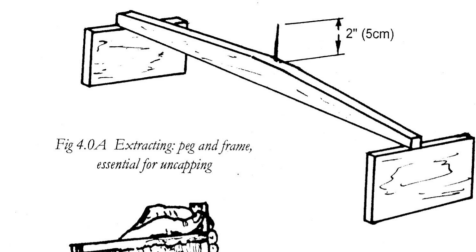

2" (5cm)

*Fig 4.0A Extracting: peg and frame,
essential for uncapping*

and cut to give the bowl small overhead and width clearances. The centre piece of timber, at least, is ideally of hardwood, and all edges rounded and smoothed so that it is the more readily cleaned before and after use. A bridge is constructed with the timber. The hardwood cross bar is drilled in the centre to take a four inch nail, with a drive fit, so that the nail tip points vertically upwards. Drill the hole too small so that you have to hammer the nail in. The nail, or peg, supports the frame by the middle of one of its side bars, and takes the weight while you knife off the cappings. I've never seen one of these available commercailly so you've little choice than but to make your own.

*Fig 4.0B Extracting: uncapping,
keeping the fingers back*

Rather than uncapping upwards, and risking cut fingers, consider slicing from the bottom up to halfway, on both sides, then upending the comb and slicing up to halfway again. Well worth a try!

These prize cappings, collected in the bowl, usually comprise at least 80% honey. A straining stint here can thus be useful (see chapter 4.2). Prize, because these are the quality products of a hive that the exhibitors use to win prizes at the shows (see chapters 4.3 and 5.1).

This is the best of your honey.
Cappings are also the best of your beeswax.

Your Different Honies

Local honey varies widely across the country, and across the world. You may be limited to your local flora, but for different flavours and maybe textures, you do have a choice of spring or summer honey. Frames of honey taken from the hives in June, that is, before the main honey flow, will contain honey that comes largely from the spring flowering plants. The flavour will be quite different from honey taken off later in the year, after the summer flow. Only the experienced tasters can assess the qualities of flavour and aroma of these two yields. I have found both sources of my local honey give very pleasant flavours.

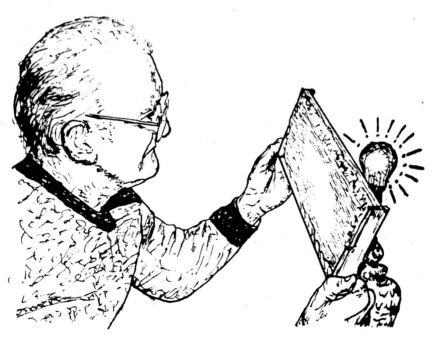

Fig 4.0C Extracting: comb and lamp, checking for light and dark areas

A honey show of any size will have light, medium and dark honey classes. With rare luck you can sometimes enter all three with honey from the same hive. Use combs of which almost all the cells are sealed. Otherwise there is a risk of too high a water content and a risk of fermentation. When the frames of sealed honey are out of the hive, shine a 60 watt lamp through each one, and note, by what light glows through, the colour of the contents of the comb. Some areas will be seen as darker than others. One of my local colleagues, found an area that was quite black. He recognised an opportunity and sent a sample off to a formal honey survey that was under way at the time. He found that 55% of his sample came from plants of a pollen classification known as C4P4. It would have been interesting to have found which species were involved.

Before embarking upon the separation process, it is worthwhile assessing whether the extra time needed is justified, whether there is enough of each to make it worthwhile. Try to estimate just how much really dark etc honey is there. Uncap firstly only the palest areas, and extract. This is your light honey. Drain out your extractor. No need to wash it out. Then uncap the medium areas, extract and drain. And the darkest areas last.

It pays to check the colours with a pair of grading glasses, available from commercial suppliers. These glasses give an assessment of colour density. One gives the density of the borderline between light and medium, the other between medium and dark, when held beside a one pound jar of honey. Don't expect a colour match though. Honey lighter than the light/ medium glass can be entered in the light honey classes in shows etc.

Fig 4.0D Extracting: checking for light, medium and dark honey

Handling and Bottling

Bulk extraction comprises slicing off the cappings and centrifuging the combs. The honey is thrown out, and splashes against, and runs down the inside faces of the enclosing tub. If you stop it, open the lid, and smell the aroma, it smells good. Great stuff! Don't get too elated though. There goes some of your flavour. In this violent process the honey has maximum contact with the air. A proportion of the volatile constituents evaporate. Some of the complex compounds, so neatly packaged and sealed when in the comb, combine readily with oxygen, and are lost in their original form. The show judges can assess this loss. However, you can retain most of this flavour difference if you extract that honey destined for the show benches another way (see chapter 4.3).

My honey, from suburbia, when extracted as described above, sets sufficiently to prevent flow when the jar is tipped onto its side, after five months. Combs of the same, but sealed, honey kept back for show purposes, give, clear

Fig 4.1A Settling Tank: Settling clears the honey. It goes in at the top, steps are needed

runny honey when similarly extracted the following year. This experience shows that exposure to air certainly accelerates granulation, and this, in spite of no change in the proportions of the various sugars.

Now you've got your honey, with or without all of its flavour. The next stage is to settle it. All the bits of propolis, of bee wings, air bubbles, but mainly of fine wax debris, float to the surface. Most of this is done within three days. It settles more completely if kept warmer during this time, or is settled for a long time. The surface debris looks like scum. It consists

Fig 4.1B Skimming off traces of wax dust with a teaspoon. Scrape the spoon with a knife.

of more wax than anything else. It is worth remembering that you have best access to skim the surface when the tank is full. You may need to spoon it off several times to clear it all. The honey is now ready to go into the jars. From the tap at the bottom of the settling tank the honey is usually quite clear, and free from any scum on the honey surface.

The last, ie top, ten pounds however, brings with it any wax dust residue remaining in the tank. Put in the jars more than the final quantity from these because you need to take more surface scum off before it is ready for sale or the show bench (see chapter 4.2).

A few days before the appointed show the honey, in the jars, is heated up to clear any vestige of granulation, and to encourage any residual fine particles to rise. This is done in a warming cabinet made for the purpose. A suitable one is described in chapter 4.5. Loosen the screw caps. A temperature of between 50degC and 60degC should be the aim. It is only necessary to maintain this final temperature for about an hour in order to ensure it has been reached throughout the contents. Measure the air temperature beside the jars with a thermometer. Much over 60degC the honey starts to darken. This is some of your sugar converting into caramel. Avoid this.

Close inspection, when the jars have cooled, will sometimes reveal the odd bubble of air still clinging to the bottom of the jar. A thin wire, 10 cm long with the end 1 cm bent at an angle, is the tool to clear this. I've even fitted a little handle to mine. It can reach through the honey to the bottom of the jar. Just the job for dislodging the most tenacious of bubbles. Push down very gently or you'll introduce yet more bubbles. No need to wait all day for them to rise to the surface either. The wire can be used to manipulate a bubble, once dislodged, from bottom to top. I can now do this 20 seconds. Wash up the wire each time you use it. Lastly, inspect the surface of the honey, and spoon off the last traces of scum, and to adjust levels so that they are common to each jar in a batch.

Fig 4.1C Releasing air bubbles in the honey jar by
poking them with a fine wire

Filtering

For several years all I needed to do to produce clear honey was to settle it for a couple of days and then run it into the jars. No filtering was required. Then came a year with a load of crystals which sank to the jar bottoms. Heating, as when clearing granulation, wouldn't dissolve them. Nor did it release them from sticking on the bottom. I hooked one or two crystals out and tasted them. They crunched up easily and dissolved. I took it as a lesser known sugar, but learned soon after that it was glucose. I had no filtering equipment suitable for this. Furthermore, I was booked to set up a beekeeping stand at a local show in only a week or so, including honey for sale, and thus the urgency was pressing and the following pressurised honey filter was pieced together. At short notice it solved the problem, but a simpler solution was discovered later (see later in this chapter: Crystals in Your Honey?).

A Pressurised Honey Filter

A 2 litre plastic fizzy drink bottle was used with its bottom cut off. It will accept at least 4 lb honey. The pump is a Progress "Fizzkeeper", purchased locally. The only item necessary to buy. Actually, I'd had mine in the house for a month or two. A close weave fabric is the filter element of the gadget, fixed with epoxy. Elastic bands help with the fixing. The fabric can be washed and used again and again. Only honey jars, a plastic funnel, the supporting frame - easy to make, the central stage, with a central aperture, supports the bottle and lifts out - and the receiving container, a cleaned out, 4 litre, ice cream tub, are needed to complete the kit.

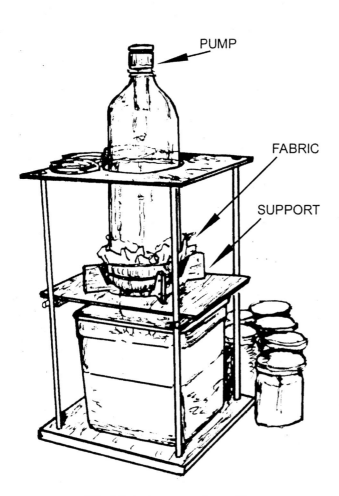

PUMP

FABRIC

SUPPORT

Fig 4.2A A pressure honey filter

Usage

It is better to skim off any wax from the surface first. There really is no need to clog the filter membrane unnecessarily. As more lots are pushed through the process takes longer.

When a batch is done or when the filter needs cleaning, the receiver pot is taken out and replaced temporarily with a bowl or a saucer. The pump is removed and the bottle turned upside down to drain, and the textile mesh can then be washed and dried, with the epoxy still in place, and used again and again.

It speeds up filtering if the honey is first warmed. I found twenty pumps to be about right. It doesn't pay to over pressurise the bottle. It will shorten the pump life.

Crystals in Your Honey?

Sometimes you see crystals scattered across the bottoms of the honey jars. The case described above was such. Situations also arise in which a layer of fine crystals settles to over an inch deep. I never forget when away on holiday once, seeing local honey displayed for sale in a shop window. The top half inch was clear. The remainder appeared granulated.

These are glucose crystals. If you heat the mix, and stir, the crystals will all dissolve into the honey. In fact, it is not even necessary to take the lid off the jar, unless using a microwave. Just sit the jar in hot water; not boiling. I use a warming cabinet, a dry process, about 55degC for about an hour. Then shake the jar actively until all the crystals disappear. It works. If you can't bear to keep your fingers immersed in it, the water is too hot.

My attempts to filter the honey through a Jar Attachment Feeder never worked. The mesh was too fine for any useful flow. I prised apart the two halves of the filter, cut the hole bigger to 2.2 inches (5.6cm) diameter and glued the two halves together again, but with a coarse mesh

Fig 4.2B A honey jar feeder modified to house a more open, 7 per inch (2.5cm), mesh

between. This was stainless steel mesh, at 7 meshes per inch (2.5cm), an offcut from the varroa screens I made. The joint was sealed on the outside with epoxy.

One jar is filled with the waxy honey. The special filter screwed on to the top, and a clean jar screwed onto the top of that. The whole assembly is up-ended, but nothing will ever happen until the combination is tilted to one side. Then a large bubble can be seen to rise through the honey in the top jar. This is the start of all the honey in the top jar flowing through the filter, leaving wax dust behind. This only takes a few minutes, when the top jar, now empty but for the wax residue, can be loaded again.

This process incurs little or no spillage.

Fig 4.2C The slickest home made filter. Works only if tilted using a wedge as shown.

Preparation of Honey for Show

Show winners, when asked how they did it, sometimes sweep away a host of concerns and lengthy attentions with a curt "You have to spend a fortnight polishing the jars". It is true that attention to detail is paramount. Much of the detail is considered here.

The classes are always for two jars, sometimes more. They, and the contents, must be exactly the same in every detail, or they don't reach the judges' short list, and the honey is not even tasted.

First of all, be warned. A sad let-down awaits any who are not familiar with the rules. Get a copy and analyse how they affect your entry, and do look closely at the entries that win when you attend the shows. See if you can seek the difference between those that achieve placings and those that don't.

It is well known among honey exponents that cappings drainings (see chapter 4.0) constitute the best honey. Of course it does. It hasn't left half its flavour behind in the extracting process, as I have just described (chapter 4.1). It hasn't had the exposure to air. So, here lies your prize winning honey. One consistent prize winner of my acquaintance took this to its conclusion. He pushed it off the comb, straight into the settling bucket.

Dislodge any air bubbles that persist in sticking to the bottom of the jar. I use the tool described in chapter 4.1 Equalise the levels with the two-knife method (fig 4.3B).

Fig 4.3A Jar bottoms: sort and select identical embossings

The Jars

Jars come in boxes of half a gross. Wash them up. Sort them into groups, each group with a common batch number. This is embossed into the base. A future prospect is an embossed dot code. Dots, numbers, or any hieroglyphics that come; learn to recognise the differences between batches. Keep the jars of any one batch together. Never enter a show class with jars from different batches.

Then inspect each jar closely, looking for chips, bubbles in the glass, knots, striations, in fact any imperfections.

The lids must be clean, free from scratches and any other flaws, and of a common colour. Ensure that they are quite identical. Give the plastic seals a scrutiny. Prepare about six jars more than the class requires, leaving the final selection to as late as is practical.

Fig 4.3B Two knife method: equalise honey levels with two knives.
Each scrapes the other clear

The last stages are to stick the class labels on, and to fit clean, new lids. Some exhibitors leave the fitting of a clean new set of screw tops until arrival at the show.

The label must always be fixed between the two vertical seams in the glass that divide the jar into two. See that the label on each is positioned the same way with respect to the embossed numberings that are always to be seen on the jar bottoms. Stand the jars together with the labels touching, to see that they are at exactly the same height.

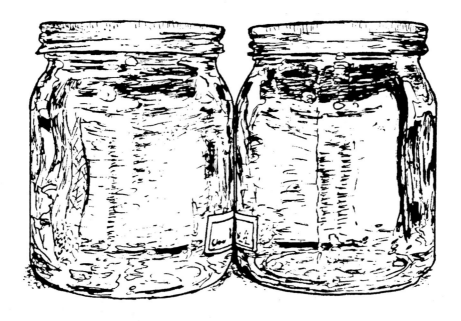

Fig 4.3C Two matching labels. Check that they are at the same height

Spin Drier Conversion (for separating cappings)

Cappings, as collected in a bowl, contains several times more honey than wax. Much of the honey can be recovered simply by draining overnight. Even after this, the residue still comprises more honey than wax. A useful further separation can be achieved by the use of a modified spin drier. I've heard that it will also extract heather honey. The method has merit in being a cold process.

Our old spinner didn't owe us anything. Its motor had been renewed within our memory. We bought a new one for the washing. It had a stainless steel drum. This released the old one for the modifications described here. You may have enough use to justify a new spin dryer for the cappings.

Repair

The whole machine must first be dismantled and inspected for deterioration, wear and tear. Jammed screws must be removed, restored and replaced where necessary, flaking paint removed. Rusty areas must be tidied up, treated and painted over. Rusted through holes can be skinned across with fibreglass using car body repair techniques. Then the whole machine can benefit by a cleaning up and a coat of paint where needed. The cleaning is particularly important on the drum, which comes into contact with the honey. I removed the push rod that is used to disengage the brake pads, and skinned over the hole in the spinner floor, through which it works, with fibreglass. The springs in the brake pad housing, and the clockwork cover release timer were also left out. This takes out the fast stop facility which is a hindrance when dismantling and reassembling. Do remember that this makes it an ostensibly unsafe machine.

Conversion

The inside of the casing, i.e. all the surfaces that will contact the honey are then lined with fibreglass.

You will need:
    Fibreglass sheet, 300g / sq m
    Surface tissue (a thinner fibreglass sheet)
    Resin H
    Catalyst
    Acetone, 500mL
    Pigment. White.
    Brush, 1.5 inch (38mm)
    Graduated syringe, 1cc
    Disposable vinyl protective gloves

These materials can all be obtained from The Fibreglass Shop (see suppliers list). I found them very helpful. They sell a resin, and fibreglass craft guide booklet for £2-50, and will send you a price list on request.

The fibreglass pieces are cut to shape beforehand, a round piece with a hole in it for the base, and a long rectangle for the sides. A planned overlap of the edges does ensure a continuity of coverage. The order is:

1) Initial resin coat
2) Layer of 300g / sq m fibreglass
3) Brush in more resin
4) Leave to set
5) Rub down
6) Another resin coat
7) Layer of surface tissue
8) Brush in resin
9) Leave to set
10) More rubbing down
11) Final resin coat.

The casing is first painted with a thin coat of resin. Then apply the fibre sheet straight away onto the freshly applied resin so that it can be slid into the exact intended spot. The syrupy resin yields to this moving.

I found that a 1% catalyst mix sets in the hot sun, tack free, in half a day, where a 2% mix stays slightly tacky for two or three days without the sun's help. Here lies an advantage which you can make use of. Deliberately make a 2% catalyst for coats prior to placement of the thin fibreglass. I used this to great advantage with a 13 X 45 inches (33 X 115cm) piece of surface tissue. It is as flimsy as tissue paper. I pulled it off and offered it back to the inside of the casing about ten times, until I was satisfied it was exactly where I intended it.

Once positioned, more resin must then be brushed on. This sinks into the fibreglass sheet which becomes totally embedded. Then the air bubbles can be seen. They must be sought and released. A rub down with glass paper between each layer removes all the whiskers and levels any small protruberances.

A finer finish is achieved when a sheet of surface tissue is applied on top in the same way. This is a thinner and finer grade of fibreglass that doesn't show the swirly strand patterns and leaves a smoother surface.

It pays to put a little pigment in each layer for good obliteration. When mixing the resin, I dripped in about 5% of the white pigment into a plastic pot recycled from the kitchen. Then, with the use of a weighing machine, I poured in the estimated amount of resin. Then you can add 1 or 2% of catalyst and start mixing. 80 g for a brushed coat over the whole of the spinner inside, will give you a starting figure. The brush must be cleaned soon after use with acetone. Then, with the surplus coaxed out, it is next treated with a proprietary brush cleaner liquid. Thus the brush life is considerably extended. If the vinyl gloves contact the acetone, they just shrivel up.

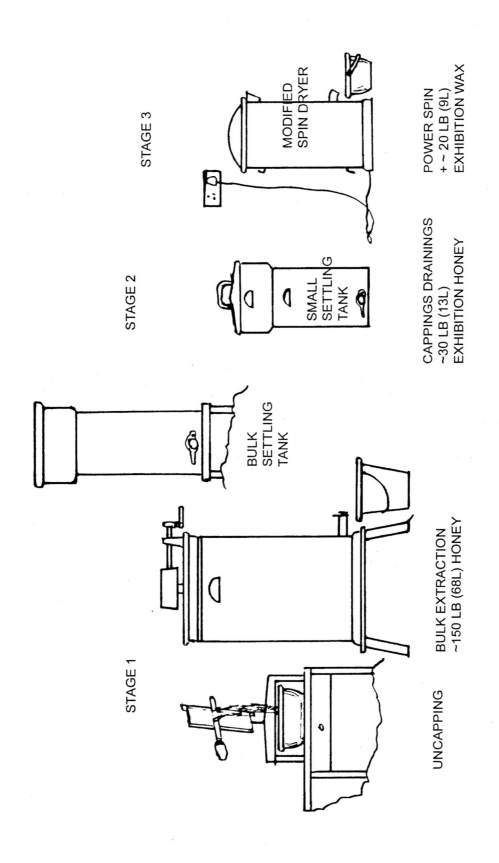

STAGE 3

MODIFIED SPIN DRYER

POWER SPIN
+ ~ 20 LB (9L)
EXHIBITION WAX

STAGE 2

SMALL SETTLING TANK

CAPPINGS DRAININGS
~30 LB (13L)
EXHIBITION HONEY

BULK SETTLING TANK

STAGE 1

BULK EXTRACTION
~150 LB (68L) HONEY

UNCAPPING

Fig 4.4 The extracting plan for cappings: exhibition quality honey and wax culminating in final extraction using a converted spin drier

It is worth a mention that measuring and recording the proportions at each stage is the key to consistent and predictable results. A 1 cc graduated syringe is indispensable for measuring the small quantities of catalyst.

All this should ideally be finished at least three months before intended use. This is because it takes this sort of time for the smell of the styrene from the resin to fade to insignificance, even when encouraged to clear with some occasional hot wash-downs.

In use the inside vertical faces of the barrel must be lined with an open mesh material that doesn't crush under pressure. This provides a flow path under the wax for the honey. I used a rectangle of stainless steel mesh sized 13 x 40 inches (330 x 1015mm) that I had around. A muslin bag was made to contain the wax cappings.

Usage

There is only speed control by switching off the spinner, unless you buy anA mains, electronic speed controller. This was tried, to turn the spin speed down and adjust as required. But my advice is to see how you get on without it before you make any purchase. The range of control is limited, and it needs to be removed completely to achieve the fastest spinner speed. I found that with the cappings drained overnight, the honey left in each load for the spinner to handle is hardly enough to flood into the motor compartment below. These controllers only work on motors of the commutator type, not on induction motors. You can of course, always turn the spinner off for a minute or two to allow a build up of honey to clear. I found it unnecessary.

The wax retained in the drum was almost dry, and when rendered into a block in the solar panel, yielded so little honey residue that this wasn't worth saving. I just soaked it off by immersing the wax block in a bucket of water to dissolve the honey away.

The honey spun out is a bit more involved. What you get from suburbia honey will be a variation of the following form depending entirely upon the intrinsic qualities of your local honey.

Froth (on the top): Looks like meringue. The froth is made of honey. I was quite unable to reduce this to liquid, and eventually put it into a pot to spread on my fresh bread and butter.

Honey (in the middle): Heavily loaded with fine wax particles. This honey may be cleared by settling, where the wax floats to the top. Mine wouldn't, whereas that from the bulk extraction did. I eventually bottled it and heated each honey jar to about 55degC and skimmed the wax from the top with a teaspoon.

Clear Honey (at the bottom): Honey processed by this means is inclined to set even earlier than that obtained from a conventional extractor.

A Warming Cabinet

My honey warming box has proved so indispensable that it has justified a permanent, ready-to-use, placement in my sanctum of resources. Granulated honey needs to be warmed to 50 degrees C for the granulation to clear. Using this method of gently heat can take up to 6 hours. Although this warming box was purposed originally and specifically for clearing granulated, or granulating honey, I have used it also for warming foundation prior to fitting into frames, and prior to rolling candles; otherwise quite unmanageable on a frosty day. Further alternative uses tried are the encouragement of epoxy resin to harden quicker, and for warming a yeast starter for mead making. And with further modifications, I also now use it to help cast a block of wax. No doubt some of my readers will be inspired to reach for saws and chisels, and will find yet further uses.

Before we consider the details of this project we must first understand the important principle upon which its design is based.

The principle explained

A honey pot, or any pot come to that, sitting directly upon a heater, is warmed by three transmission media, as I was taught in 'science'. Conduction, convection and radiation. Conduction and radiation are too localised, too fast, for this purpose. The bottom of the jar gets overcooked while the top is still cold. You might even crack the jar using conduction and/ or radiation. In order to block the direct effects of these two, the honey pots are sat upon a heat resisting, heat insulating table. These pots are thus heated solely by air currents which go round the sides of the table. This is by convection.

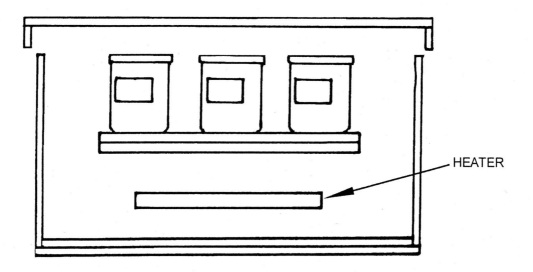

Fig 4.5A Warming the Honey: avoid direct heating

There are plenty of other ways of heating honey. Different systems do it more quickly, more cheaply, or are more suited to handling tonnes of honey. A microwave will do it in a few seconds. But remember to remove the metal screw cap first if you use a microwave.

This convection system is ideally suited to be set up at home. A heat insulating table of just 10 inches (25cm) square holds nine, one-pound (454 g) jars nicely, with small spaces between the jars for the warm air to circulate. Standing the jar of honey in warmed water is quicker but the temperature must be carefully limited, and this has the disadvantage of ruining any labels, leaving water marks and running the remote risk of diluting the honey or cracking the jar.

Most building boards used for ceilings and partitions contain a high proportion of gypsum. This is why they are exceptionally good for tolerating high temperatures and for fire resistance. Sheets of it are placed above (see fig 4.5C) and below the heat source in order to

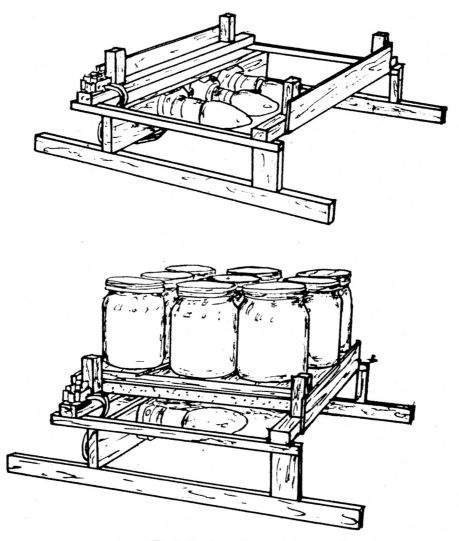

Fig 4.5B (top) The basic frame and
Fig 4.5C (bottom) the frame with heat insulating square of
gypsum rich plaster board and nine jars

prevent overheating the nearby timbers. I use three, lozenge-shaped, bayonet lamps, each of 40 watts, as heaters. One can, of course, use fewer or lower wattage lamps for more modest warming applications. These lamps are heat buffered above and below with these partition type boards.

A plywood box 16.5 inches (42cm) square and 11.5 (30cm) high is sufficient to house all. Mine (see fig 4.5D) was made with redundant timber that I had around. These dimensions give sufficient space around the sides of the ten inch insulating table for the heated air to circulate. A 250 watt dimmer switch is connected in to control the lamps. This enables the heat to be turned down to any level as required, simply by adjusting the control knob.

At full power the total heating time from 'switch on' to 'switch off' took around six hours. Now, the adjustments needing attention and discretion occurred only during the last two hours of this total, dependent upon temperature readings and the clarity of the honey. Eventually my system included a time switch which turns the heater to 'ON' at about three o'clock in the middle of the night. I then needed to read the thermometer and make honey inspections and heating adjustments at about breakfast time. I was thus freed to go about my business next day without being committed at home to monitor the process.

Fig 4.5D   The enclosing box with dimmer control. Ply cover not shown

Beeswax

As the beekeeping years tick by, one's accumulation of beeswax builds up, and eventually one must opt for a constructive and expedient method of using it.

The working time of even the uncommitted or a retired do-it-yourselfer is to be costed. With this in mind he must choose one of the following alternatives that the time and expense that he invests justifies. Once rendered into blocks, he can decide to handle it no further. After all, it can be regarded as a messy and gummy threat to domestic tranquility, that should be avoided. In this case it must be appreciated that it is marketable. It can be exchanged by most beekeeping suppliers, for foundation, or for other beekeeping goods. This can work very well but the cost of postage, or the round trip to the works can make this arrangement uneconomic, so it must be balanced against the prospect of making one's own foundation from the wax, or by arranging for such trading to take place at a convenient beekeeping show. Immerse it first in a bucket of water for an hour or so. This will dissolve any sticky honey residue from the surface. Dry and wrap it and thus barter it.

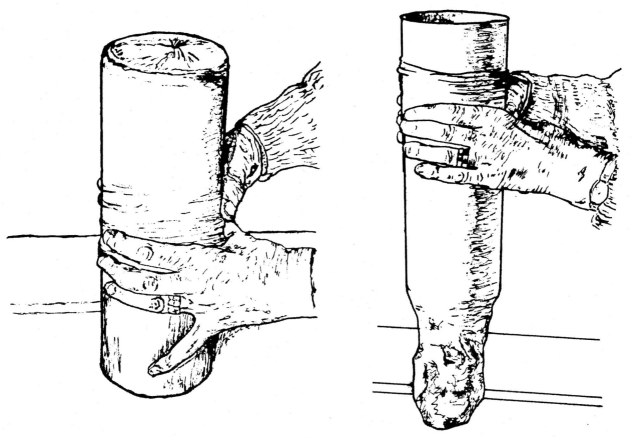

Fig 5.0A (left) Pulling tights over a 4 inch (10 cm) plastic tube
Fig 5.0B (right) Loading the tights with wax bits and bumping them down

Beeswax from the Solar Panel

Many beekeepers melt their old comb into wax blocks using solar heat (see chapter 6.0), or in the oven. If the solar melted block is the result of fits and starts sunshine then honey is often trapped between layers.

A very high quality of wax can be achieved within home processing if one follows the initial rendering with a second process using a suitably fine filtering treatment. The solar panel must be cleaned out. See also Chapter 5.1: Preparing the frames and solar panel, p 139. Remove every scrap of propolis and other persistent dross. The blocks of wax to be filtered are broken into small pieces and stuffed into the good halves of discarded nylon tights. A good sunny day will see several of these enlarged sausages melt and filter through the fine mesh. Weigh them first and satisfy yourself that it will not overfill your receptor pot.

Beeswax is usually a nice pale yellow-brown, but the colour varies delicately from source to source, and from batch to batch. Decorative items made from beeswax, such as candles, moulded figures and plaques, and even foundation within reason, all look far more presentable in the paler shades. So the wax enthusiast, having produced only a small block of a darker shade of wax is understandably loath to mix it with his bulk quantities. It is best to put it aside until enough has been accumulated to be worthwhile filtering and to find another use.

Uses can be found for darker wax where the colour is immaterial, e.g. the carpet trade, to ease pulling the threads through, in the retuning of accordion type musical instruments in which sets of reeds are set in beeswax and spend their useful lives in the dark, or you can even use it for your own foundation. It is possible to collect a long list of uses for which people buy beeswax. Only a few insist on the lighter colours.

You can lighten the colour of beeswax for most decorative purposes with hydrogen peroxide (H_2O_2). Coggleshall & Morse (1995). It is necessary to heat the wax in a double saucepan to a close approach to 100degC. It is then stirred actively while dripping the hydrogen peroxide into it slowly.

Fig 5.0C Wax bits in a stocking: recycled tights make a superior, fine wax filter

You will need. -

A double saucepan, water betwee the inner and outer pans
heat source
A thermometer for wax
An electric motor, suitably and safely mounted
An impeller, with a round, concentric outer edge
50cc of 30% hydrogen peroxide. (H_2O_2) This is the maximum concentration
normally sold in any pharmacy
A 10cc plastic syringe

10cc H_2O_2 into 600g wax will make a small change of colour. 20cc will make a noticable change. Pour a sample of your wax into an aluminium foil mould, a milk bottle top? to compare it before and after treatment. You will then be able to see the difference.

The companies which refine beeswax in large quantities import most, if not all of the wax, and sell a lovely, partly bleached wax to many users, known as 'Non-BP'. They also bleach it white for most of their output.

Another method of lightening the colour of your wax, and at the same time extending your quantity, is to buy some from one of the established wax refiners and mix it with some of

Fig 5.0D Long wax spout: a spout is built up with bits of wax, dipping and carving

your supply. Their 'Non BP' grade is partly bleached and suitable for foundation and candle making. Most of the wax I process and sell is a 50% mix, half from my hives and half non-BP. It follows that, with planned, mixed proportions, wax can be produced in any of a range of shades.

When finished working with beeswax and wanting to empty a saucepan of it, the aluminium foil trays of the type that are frequently used for Chinese takeaway food are very good to pour out into. This is because the wax is easy to release from these trays, and distributed among say eight trays it cools all the more quickly. Furthermore, a working session usually accumulates detritus and water in the wax. This settles in the bottom of the saucepan. If one pours out carefully this can be tidily decanted into the last aluminium tray and thus isolated and dealt with separately. If the trays have been used for anything before, it would be wise to check visually against a bright lamp for pin holes before using them.

Fig 5.0E Pouring out: ending a session dispensing into foil trays

tag 5.1 Casting a Block of Wax

Casting a Block of Wax

Most shows include a class calling for a block of wax of high quality. Sounds easy enough, but don't be fooled. You may have quality wax. You've still to learn how to come up with best selected and filtered wax and then to cast an immaculate block from it. Tiny bits of dirt have an amazing persistence for turning up on the bottom surface of your carefully protected wax. I was put off for several years once after breaking a pyrex bowl in knocking a block of wax out of it. It just would not come away. Also, lumps and cracks often appear on the block surface during the cooling process. Several other stumbling blocks await your discovery. Further to this, the overall aim of least melting must be recognised and kept in mind. The more and longer you melt it the more that lovely smell of beeswax fades. This unique and attractive quality of beeswax is nice to preserve. It follows that if you can get the finished product to the show bench; if you can sell the product to the customer, with least melting, the more of this natural quality is retained. Then you have preserved to the utmost this natural and delicate distinction special only to beeswax.

Modified Warming Cabinet (to become a Cooling Cabinet)

The answer to cracking and distortion lies largely in a very slow cooling rate such that the temperature in the centre of the block differs but little from that at the extremities during the critical times of the cooling. In order to control this cooling rate I devised modifications to my warming (and cooling) cabinet described earlier (chapter 4.5) to achieve:

1) a higher maximum temperature. 80degC, instead of the 60degC which is adequate for clearing honey.

2) a pointer on the control knob to read against an arbitrary scale or graduation. This is to give a predictable setting, thus to enable any process to be accurately repeated.

Fig 5.1A Modifications to the warming box (see chapter 4.5):
two additional 60 watt lamps and an interchangeable baseboard housing an impeller

The modifications were to provide a tighter control of cooling, and from a higher temperature than that needed just for honey. Two extra lozenge shaped lamps were fitted, these of 60 watts each, and all five controlled by the dimmer knob.

Also a small shaded pole mains motor fitted with a home-carved wooden propeller to circulate the air, this was fitted as shown in fig 5.1A to give a higher degree of temperature uniformity across the interior. A hole with a grommet fitted, just under the top cover, allows access for a thermometer to monitor closely the temperature within.

The controller knob is then calibrated. Its shaft bears a moulded flat side which ensures a location when the knob is replaced. A pointer is fitted to the knob, and a scale made to fit behind it. The scale can be marked with the temperature that one finds that it stabilizes to, or marked, as I did, with an arbitrary, linear scale, say 0 to 100. Mine was laboriously made and marked by hand and reads 1 to 13, with divisions at 0.1 intervals. Then about five points may be calibrated, making a note of the ambient room temperature at the time. This gives enough data to draw a useful graph.

Having done this, the warming cabinet has now been upgraded into a scientific instrument. One that can be relied upon for planned processing.

Wax Preparation Process

Then, with the foregoing in mind, consider the summary below of the whole wax preparation process. Each stage removes a further proportion of solid, impurity matter. Each stage adds to the clean-up. Some stages may be omitted, rearranged, or doubled up as your observations and assessments dictate.

Process 1   Melt. Solar panel. Old combs, or cappings. Coarse filter.

Process 2   Soak the block in a bucket of water to remove traces of honey.

Process 3   Cold carving. If the block is thick enough much woolly dross and fine traces of dirt can be carved or scraped from the underside. Warm it a little for this. It makes for easier carving.

Process 4   Melt. Solar panel. Filter through nylon stockings or tights. An essential stage.

Process 5   Filter through lint

Process 6   Filter through filter paper

Process 7   Casting through fabric. This includes the controlled cooling process

Here, you see, it has already been melted down five times. Cold carving can be introduced between any of the melting stages, as inspection demands, and may enable one melting stage to be skipped. I devised the fabric filter initially to remove the lesser dirt that survived the nylon tights routine, but found it more useful for the final casting as it prevents the ingress of airborne dusts and bits by any other spurious routes. Although a considerable improvement can be expected, finer residual bits can still be detected. Any quantities may be selected to suit one's available containers in all but the last process, when the wax will be weighed.

Preparing Frames and the Solar Panel Wax

I usually render old combs in my solar panel by including the frames and all. But I first scrape the propolis off the lug ends, and anywhere else that it appears upon the frames. I also scrape out most of the gummy gunge from the solar tray frequently when it's cooler. This is because, once the propolis is mixed with the wax, there is no known method that will separate it. Traces in the wax contribute to release problems when moulding. I know that if I clear out this gum whenever I can, then I can enhance the general quality of my wax. You can too. However, the best quality wax is from cappings, largely because it contains least propolis. Neither is it tainted with the by-products of brood generation. So clean out your solar box before you render cappings. Use boiling water and a scraper. Get it spotless. Identify the resulting wax. Stick a label on it and keep it separate from other wax. I normally filter all my wax through nylon tights in a second solar panel process. The panel is first scoured and mopped until it is gleaming. The descriptions to follow achieve further, yet finer, cleaning up. Small residuals of dross and bits, all of which sink obligingly to the bottom of a melted block, can be scraped or carved off without any further heating.

The Ideal Bowl

A good casting bowl can be of enamel ware or of borosilicate glass (Pyrex; Phoenix), or earthenware. Other types can be considered as long as the inside surface is smooth and shiny and the release prospects are satisfactory. The inside faces should have no grooves or ridges, only smooth curves. A continuous rim with a lip is essential, no pouring lip, and no extensions or handle at rim level. Car boot sales offer prospects of a chance find. If you have any choice (rarely!), the one made of the lowest heat conducting material is best. Metal feels cold to the touch. This is not because it is any colder than things made of wood or plastic. It is because it conducts the heat away from your hand so much faster. It is therefore a poor choice for this purpose and herein lies the answer to the cracks that appear in the block no matter how slowly it is cooled. This principle was finally driven home to me when I cast one pound (454g) blocks for sale into a thin plastic mould, and left them to cool naturally in the room. These never cracked. All the others, cast in heavier, metal or glass bowls, did. The bowl I use for one pound (454g) blocks is white, enamelled, and measures 7.5" (190mm) across the rim, and is 3.4" (8.9mm) deep.

My experience with wax cooling is that cracks occur within the periphery of a block after it is poured into a bowl and left to cool in still air, the outer edges, being in close contact with the bowl surface, lose heat to it far faster than that lost from the top surface. This effect can be buffered in part by insulating the outer surface of the bowl. By this means the prolonged cooling time needed in order to avoid these cracks can be safely shortened.

These earthenware, glass and stove enamelled metal bowls conduct the heat away from those surfaces of the wax in immediate contact ten time faster than is released by air convection from the top face. It is probably nearer a hundred times faster. Look for a bowl that is warmest to the touch. But never mind all this. With a bit of insulation and much slower than natural cooling we can contain some of this imbalance.

Release

I use an enamelled bowl quite a lot. This was the only one I could find having the right dimensions for a one pound (454g) block. I first smeared the inside faces with a film of washing up liquid, although it is worth a try without a release film of any sort, because it can only contaminate the wax, and the judges may be able to smell it. I then tried without, and was pleased to find that it wasn't needed. One block, for example, that I cast without a priming film, I topped with a half inch of water when cool, and put in the refrigerator over the nights. It spent the intervening days at room temperature in the kitchen. After four days, it floated out. This soon became my standard method. Since then I've not had one that wouldn't come away.

You might have to wait seven days for it. If this isn't fast enough you can always divide your day into three, eight-hour stints and apply your alternate cooling and thawing treatment into alternate stints. I've never tried waiting, to see if it comes away without the temperature cycling. There is nothing to gain by a session in a freezer, as this will set the water solid and prevent seepage between wax and bowl. Clean out traces of wax from the bowl between castings, with white spirit, and follow this with a washing up.

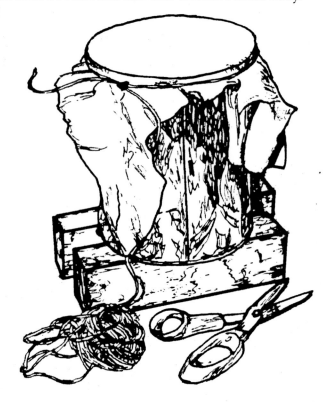

Lint Filtering (Padmore)

Finer traces of dirt are removed by filtering through lint. Cut the top and bottom out of a tin can. Leave a turned edge on at the bottom as this enhances the diameter with a small ridge at the bottom

Fig 5.1B Fitting the lint. The blocks are to lift the wire handle clear of the table

edge which helps to retain the string tie. Make two holes opposite each other near the top. Bend some thick wire through these to form a suspending loop. Tie a skin of lint across the bottom, downy side towards the inside. I use an elastic band to hold the lint in position while I tie two turns of string round. It must be tight. Cut off the surplus lint. Remove the elastic band. It doesn't like the heat and falls into your filtered wax. I further secure the lint by rubbing in some epoxy under the string after tying. Hang the can from the top, inside the oven. Place a suitable receptacle under the can and set the oven to WARM. You can keep putting more blocks of wax into the can, but weigh the overall quantity beforehand to suit the capacity of the receiving pot. 4 lb (1.8Kg) through this treatment takes about 8 hours. The electric oven that I use has a fan built in, and bits of dust still get blown in. The rate of flow, being dependent upon the depth of the liquid, reduces to little more than a trickle. The last 50 to 100 g always seems to stay put; it takes so long.

Through Filter Paper

This is just the same as through lint, but laboratory filter paper is fitted above the lint. Use Whatman's no.4 (available from laboratory equipment suppliers). This is claimed to retain particles of 20 to 25µm. The lint serves only to support the paper. This process takes yet longer.

The Final Casting Through Fabric

A firther, yet more sophisticated adaptation of this process is described later in this chapter under the section 'Getting Serious: Entering National Shows'.

A filter element can be made from a range of textile materials. I have used part of an old shirt, and parachute silk. The fabric is to be tied across the top of the receiving bowl. The selected garment should have been washed many times during its life so that it releases no more textile traces. A circular piece is cut out about 2 inches (50mm) greater diameter than the lip of the casting bowl. Make a written note of which saucepan lids you sneak from the kitchen to draw the circles round. This will save you that endless searching next time. To thread a string through, the holes should be pierced on a pitch circle of about an inch (25mm) greater diameter than the bowl lip.

I found that the holes punch cleaner if the material is backed by paper or thin card. Give the fabric piece a good shaking before use. The many small pieces punched out have an irritating way of getting into the cast block of wax.

The piece of fine-weave cloth, threaded with string, is stretched across the open top and tied round under the edge with string. The centre is pushed down, about 0.5 inch (13mm) in the middle. Sufficient wax is then prepared by weighing. Add about 1/4 ounce (7g) to allow for that absorbed by the cloth. A proportion of the wax is stood on the filter cloth. Put it in the oven and set the heat to WARM (185 - 195 deg F; 85 - 90degC). An electric oven is preferred. Gas ovens release water vapour and can introduce tiny spots of water in a block. This leaves little blow holes. Put the rest of the wax on as it melts and sinks away. A pound (0.5Kg) of wax should take about two hours to melt and go through. The fabric system is closed. No pouring. No chance of ingress of specs or floating dusts or hairs. Thus, perfect for the final casting. Open the oven each half hour just enough to peek in, and monitor the melting progress. The fan in my oven is an asset as it gives uniform heating, but it is suspected of blowing dust around. I might have to introduce filter paper to this stage if fine dust still gets in.

When all has passed through the cloth, the basin is carefully lifted out with gloves, and sat into the already heated, levelled, warming cabinet. The warming cabinet lid is removed for no more seconds than is necessary to install the pot of wax. This is because opening the top

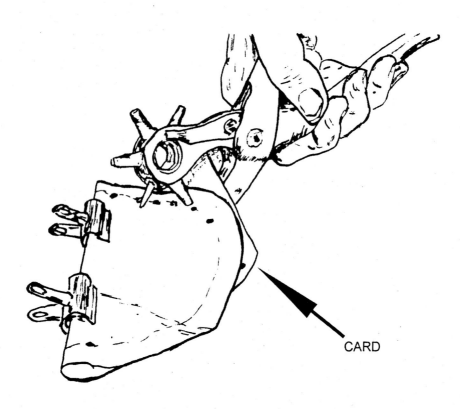

CARD

Fig 5.1C Clipping the material, backed by card: perforating the fabric

causes a dramatic fall in temperature. Get a willing assistant to lift the lid off for you when you say "now", and replace it quickly. Any lost temperature quickly restores.

Cooling Control

Set the temperature control that will give 65degC, and leave it there for an hour, or even more. Make fine adjustments if necessary to keep it the temperature constant.   This is in order to prevent any part of the wax from falling below 64degC while that of the core falls from about 80degC to much closer to 64degC. After one hour the control can be adjusted to reduce the temperature by small increments of 1degC each quarter of an hour, down to 55degC, and doubling this rate below 55degC until the temperature has fallen to 40degC. The heating can then be turned off. The fan should stay on for a further hour. During all this time the top cover must not be disturbed or the temperature will fall too quickly instead of reaching room temperature at a slow, even rate.

The value of this final stage is that the inner chamber is enclosed and no extraneous dirt can get into the bowl. (Fluff and hairs etc float around in the atmosphere quite unseen). The fabric is left in place until the final block is cool enough to be inspected. The warming cabinet must first be set up in order to ensure that when the hot bowl of wax is lifted into it (within 15 seconds if possible), it can be relied upon to be level.

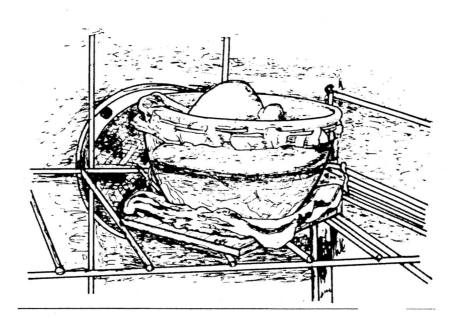

Fig 5.1D Wax bowl in the oven:
in the oven the wax drips straight into the casting bowl

Summary of the preparations to be made for the cooling process -

1.   Ensure that when the pot is placed in the warming/cooling cabinet, it will be level.
     Use a spirit level beforehand. You don't have time for adjustments during the
     transfer.
2.   The bowl and filter membrane must be washed and clinically clean before tying up.
3.   The warming (cooling) cabinet is prepared. Mine, when not loaded, takes around
     two hours to approach 80degC. It takes about this same time for one pound
     of wax to melt and go through the fabric. So, I switch them on together.
4.   An assistant is useful to operate the lid of the cabinet and to replace it quickly,
     although I have done it without.
5.   The controller is then set to 65degC and left there for an hour before introducing
     graded reductions of temperature.

Polishing

The attraction of a cast block, in the eyes of all judges, can be enhanced with a shine on the rounded surface. Whatever process you use, the block surfaces must be protected from scratches. Once marked thus, you might as well go back to the beginning. I hold the block with

Fig 5.1E Filter strainer assembly: composite filter comprising, from top: 6.5 inch (16.5 cm) strainer with filter (preferred) paper in it, wooden lift-off frame, casting bowl with fabric tied across and plywood baseboard

a plastic film while I skim it briskly with an old cotton garment. Some other fabrics I've used seem to cling. I have done better by cooling the block in the refrigerator before going about the polishing. This makes the wax harder and it thus takes a polish better. A similar exercise with a block straight out of the freezer was complicated by condensation, although trials in this respect may well be worth pursuing.

This process of wax preparation won me first prize and a trophy at the Surrey County Show of 1999, out of 10 entries. Furthermore, the judges being suitably impressed, also awarded it the Blue Ribbon: Best Entry in the Show. At the time I was aware of several more refinements that could be made to further approach the ideal, this event being one stage in an ongoing programme to match the top performers. A further step in a studied enhancement of techniques. This gave me confidence to enter for the open class at the National where the competition is an order stiffer.

Getting Serious: Entering National Shows

A scheme to embody the filter paper into the final casting stage was devised. I had such paper of 7.3 inches (18.5cm) diameter. This was insufficient to span across the bowl. So I modified an 7 inch (18cm) kitchen strainer. The kitchen got a new one. I got the old one. The wire handle was cut off and the bottom of the mesh was flattened to 4.7 inches (12cm) diameter. The edges of a filter paper disc were folded up to form a shallow cup to fit snugly into the strainer. The sides were about 1.2 inches (3cm) high. This composite strainer was set just clear of the fabric by a specially fashioned wooden stand, albeit made of scrap wood.

How Much Wax to Start With?

A small proportion of the wax doesn't reach the casting bowl. It gets left behind in parts of the filter en route. This and other losses must be itemised and assessed in each attempt to cast a block. Following each casting, the fabric, and paper tray and strainer are weighed and recorded. Only in this way can the right amount be weighed out for a starting quantity. One must expect about 20g of wax to be retained in the fabric + filter paper + strainer. In addition to this another 100 g must be added because the last of the wax flow slows down due to the reducing depth of the residual pool. I reasoned to allow 3 hours after the last piece of wax is put into the filter, before the change over to the cooling stage is made. These extras must be added to the nominal final figure. This, in order to calculate a starting weight. This final figure is taken from the schedule of the class into which the entry is planned to be placed. One class I go in for calls for a block of 454g minimum. Another specifies limits of 425 to 480g. So, if the latter is the targetted class, the middle figure is 454g, and I needed to start with 454g+20g+100g=574g.

Refinements

I set about a third of this wax into the filter system as shown in figure 5.1E. The wooden baseboard makes for easier handling when hot and houses four studs which prevent the bowl from sliding off during handling. I place it ready into the electric oven, with the oven set to 300, a setting which must be ascertained by trial and error. The programmed oven timer is set to switch on at 4.30am. When I get up at just before 7am most of this is filtered through and I put in a further 2 or 3 pieces. By about 9am the last of the wax is put in. Three hours (12noon) later the change to cooling can take place. I control the cooling for around 6 hours to switching off the heat, but the fan is still running and I leave it until later in the evening before I take the block out, but only the flat surface can be inspected, and the release must, of necessity, be a matter for patience and temperature cycling as described earlier in this chapter ('Release', p140).

A critical, overall inspection can be applied once the block has been released and dried. Never leave finger marks. Handle the block with plastic. Finely pitted patches are often to be seen on the rounded surface, mainly down the sides. The wax missing from these pits has been left behind on the inside surface of the casting bowl.

Thus I was set back to the beginning. This, and hearing that another creditable wax entrant uses a release agent restored my acceptance of a film of detergent. I found by discussion with a previous 'open' exponent that she uses three drops and a lot of rubbing on the inside of the bowl with a detergent for improved release. I further accept that the polish I carefully achieve on my wax blocks, good as I have accomplished, does not match the gloss of those that attract the placings.

So, the semi-final lesson is to experiment. If results fail to approach the ideal, then find something else to try. An approach to a polish was achieved with a light rub over with methylated spirit on a cloth. Even a huff and a rub. Eventually best results were obtained with a brisk polish using a cotton cloth on a wax block that has been cooled in the refrigerator. My favourite cloth is old pure cotton underwear that has been washed many times since its heyday and has thus lost all its removable bits of fluff. Don't use the areas of cloth that include seams and folds. These both leave heavy pressure marks. Use just the clear areas.

Having got this far it was realised that the unpredictable element of the wax losses could be drastically cut if the bowl was weighed hot during the final minutes of filtering. The progress could then be stopped at the appropriate point in time. The composite strainer was duly set upon suitable scales while hot. The strainer, with its stand was lifted so that the reading could be taken of the weight of only the bowl and baseboard as in fig 5.1E. With three such weighings approaching the desired figure the final block weight of within 10 g of that desired was achieved.

The acknowledged winners in previous years, it must be observed, are not placed in the same order each year. They might even reach only the short list, but these placings are not recorded. It can be concluded then, that the differences in the quality, finish, refinement and presentation must be so tiny, that there is little to differentiate between any two.

Further tips that I obtained from a judge were to use a much washed silk garment for the polishing and to store the finished block immersed in honey in order to retain or enhance its aroma, rinsing off with water when needed. The sharp edge which joins the two large surfaces needs attention. It is easily damaged and must be given some smoothing attention to render the best of continuity. So a serious exhibitor can expect a placing eventually, one year, if the product be good enough, but a win cannot be assured.

There seems no shortage of ways to present the prestige, pristine wax block for show. A significant number of these measures of preparation are not obvious until one is told, and can learn from the accumulated wisdom and experience of others. A well known way of coming into contact with these techniques is to offer one's services as steward to the judges. To take this principle to its conclusion one could, of course, join the ranks of judges. After all, this unique group of specialists have to make a point of familiarity with every one of the facets of competition in each of these specialities.

And the final lesson is to keep trying, keep learning and keep entering.

Pollen

The Minute Challenge

Only the beekeeper sees the enormous quantities of pollen that his bees collect. Much of what they glean is already being, and has been, converted into new bees. But much more is stored in the hive. How can we find out more about this invisible essence of the flora? How can we protect its vulnerable transportation media between the flowers? Does pollen resist analysis by the hobbyist? No it doesn't as you will see as you read on.

The beekeeper is eminently equipped to reveal the forms, styles and qualities of these miniscule grains. This is because he has two sources of pollen not easily accessed by others:
Pollen can be collected

1)   from flowers. This will constitute a reference collection.
2)   by extraction from honey.
3)   from a pollen trap. A valuable facility hitherto widely unappreciated.

Pellets from a trap should be dried, as they are otherwise inclined to go mouldy if kept for too long. Once dried, they can be stored in dated containers and left for mounting and further study as time permits.

Much of the published literature on bee-borne pollen deals with that which is extracted from honey, with the purpose of identifying the honey source. This is not the ideal way to start studying pollen. Such pollen, when extracted using a centrifuge, and set up for viewing in the microscope consists of an extensive jumble of different species with no uniformity. Such a confusing muddle becomes an obstacle and the stopping point for most. Without consummate familiarity, the most persistent of us is usually put off for good.

Fig 5.2A A home made watch glass holder with three pegs; keeps the watch glass level.

Against this, trapped pollen is more readily studied. Fitted on a beehive for 24 hours, or even less, a pollen trap yields not only samples in abundance, but the date and the colour of the pellets can be recorded. Further, due to the honeybee's habit of constancy, any one pellet will contain enough grains of pollen for several microslides, all from one form of plant. What a unique opportunity to scan one species at a time.

Pollen of all kinds is readily processed in preparation for the microscope because the grains possess a peculiar quality of adhering to the glass surface of a microscope slide while being stained and rinsed in neat propyl alcohol, which is normally used anyway. Water must be avoided for this as it will wash all the pollen away. It is worth a mention that staining the grains does reveal surface detail to an extent to make it an essential part of the mounting process.

Most pollen mounting preparations include a swirling motion of pollen-laden alcohol in a 2inch (50mm) watch glass (fig 5.2A). The pollen concentrates into the centre.

The techniques involved in my study of pollen are too extensive to be included here, but will be produced, together with reference sources for relevant reading, in a separate publication. As in every skilled field where one hears the same story, experience is gained by doing it, and the more you do, the better you get at it.

Fig 5.2B Small bottles containing a collection of dried pollen pellets.

Making Furniture Polish

Formula

Beeswax	27 %
Turpentine	69 %
Carnauba Wax	4 %

To make 1.32 Kg polish. Enough for 15 tins, each of 3ozs (85g), or plastic pots. This quantity was to suit the capacity of my double saucepan.

Items needed: Also useful:

Plastic bucket   Small funnel
Plastic bottle   Wax thermometer.
   i.e. Empty turpentine bottle   Stirring rod
Double saucepan
Metal jug for wax
Beeswax
Carnauba Wax
Turpentine
Weighing machine
Polish container pots

Put a large kettle of water on to boil. While this is heating up, weigh 910 g of the turpentine into the spare plastic bottle (ideally, the previously emptied container) and place this bottle into the plastic bucket. Get the double saucepan of water hot and prepared for the wax, and put 53g of carnauba wax into the inner saucepan, and when it has all melted, add 356g beeswax. When the water in the kettle boils pour it into the bucket. This will warm the turpentine while the waxes melt.

When all the wax has melted, you can pour in the turpentine. If you use plastic pots it would pay to leave the resulting concoction to cool a bit before pouring out. The shape of the pots can be distorted by the heat.

In the long term the turpentine constituent has an enduring capacity to evaporate. Left on the shelf for a couple of years or more, however tightly the lid is fitted, you will find a waxy block two thirds its original diameter rattling inside the container.

Some containers made of metal are affected by traces of moisture that possibly comes with the turpentine or from your double saucepan. A year after making up, the tin shows traces of rust that makes the tin and contents worthless. Plastic pots are quite unaffected by this, but they have their own problem, in that, in prolonged contact with a turpentine rich compound some turpentine is absorbed and the pot can distort. These pots come for little difference in price, so you "pays your money and you takes your choice".

Mead

Meadmaking and winemaking utilize the same techniques. The main difference is in the source of sugars. Wine uses the sugars contained in the grapes. In home made wines the natural grape sugars are often extended or replaced with granulated (sucrose) sugar. For mead we use honey as the main sugar source.

Beekeepers so often enter the mead classes of honey shows and fail for minor reasons. This description should provide the reader with enough knowhow to compete reasonably without needing ten years of accumulated experience, and to avoid some common pit falls.

The first utter necessity is to read the rules of each specific show. It is essential that the right type of bottle carries your mead, and the cork must be exactly as required. But do seek out the mead entries at your next honey show and see if you can find any difference between those that attract the honours and those that don't.

What you will need in order to make one gallon (4.5 litres) of mead.

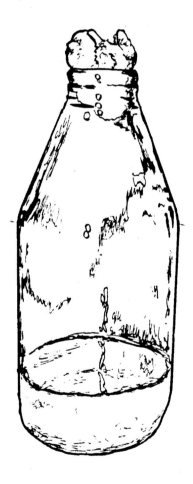

1) One gallon (4.5 litre) jar. A second jar is almost essential for siphoning
2) Fermentation lock. (Air trap)
3) Seven, one pint (27cl) bottles. Only six end up with mead in
4) Hydrometer, as for winemaking
5) Glass tube, and plastic tube for siphoning
6) Yeast, wine making type
7) Honey, approx. 2.5 pounds (1.1Kg) for dry mead. Approx. 3.5 pounds (1.6Kg) for sweet mead
8) One lemon, or citric acid powder
9) Tannin, as for wine
10) Ammonium sulphate, as activator
11) Thiamine (vitamin B), in case fermentation gets stuck
12) Sodium metabisulphite (sulphite). Sterilizer. This can be in the form of Campden tablets.

Fig 5.4.A The yeast starter in a milk bottle

Flavouring Mead

A great variety of meads may be made by pairing with flavours from other sources e.g. from flowers, fruit or spices. Fascinating end results can be achieved in this way, but care must be taken to avoid strong flavoured fruits like elderberries or strong spices, so that the subtle flavour derived from the honey is not dominated by the additions. (Ref. C Furness, 1972.)

Making a Start

Use a milk bottle, or similar, for a starter yeast solution. A cotton wool tuft set into the neck will keep flies out. Add a little yeast, and a quarter of a teaspoonful each of sugar and citric acid to four ounces of water, or preferably, follow the yeast instructions. The starter must be acid and sweet or nothing will happen. The usual additives to meet these needs are citric acid and granulated sugar. Some yeasts come as a compound complete with the necessary additional constituents. Keep the solution warm at room temperature. It should produce a froth in three to six hours when it can be added to the must (the wine preparation).

During this time the bulk must may be prepared. Fill the one gallon (4.5L) jar to 4/5 of its capacity with the following constituents.

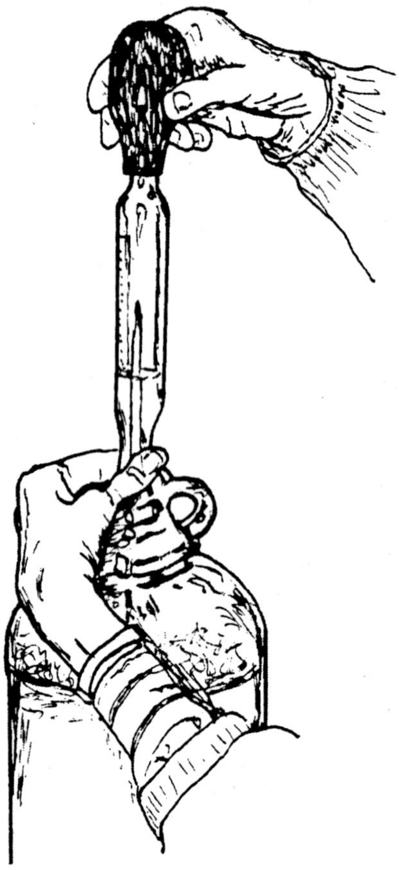

One pound (454g) of honey
The juice of one lemon, or two ounces (55g) of
    citric acid
Tannin
Ammonium sulphate, three grammes
Water (add this until the jar is 4/5 full)

Fit the fermentation lock, and put a little water in it. Flavour is retained if sulphite (item 12 in the list of ingredients) is added to the lemon juice from the moment it is squeezed from the lemon. Stir well and measure the specific gravity (SG).

Specific Gravity

The specific gravity of water is 1.0.
Winemaking SG's range from just under 1.0 to about 1.12. For winemaking parlance we forget the 1 and just use the remainder. So winemakers' figures range from about 980, which is their way of saying "minus twenty", through 0 to about 120. If a fermenting must has an SG of 5 or 10 it will taste quite sweet. 20 is too sweet. As the sugar is converted to other things this reading goes down

Fig 5.4B Mead: measuring the specific gravity (SG) using a hydrometer

towards 0, and even further to 998; less than the reading for water because we are now producing alcohol, which ia less dense and weighs less than water. The ultimate for a dry wine is about 990. That for a sweet wine is 5 to 12.

Controlling the Sugar Level

So the sixteen ounces of honey will give a starting SG of about 30. This is not critical, but record it. Fermentation normally gets under way within a few hours. When it does you will see the bubbles issuing. It ca be expected to ferment for at least three weeks. Don't add all the honey at the start, begin with just the 1lb (454g). Otherwise it sometimes causes the fermentation to stick. Measure the SG. Put more honey in before the SG goes down to 0. Measure the SG. the next day, and every second day for the following week, both before and after the honey is stirred in. As a rough guide, 4 oz (113g) honey or 5 oz (142g) granulated sugar will give an increase of 10 degrees of SG.

You will then have a record of something like this:

Date	Honey (ounces)	SG	Fall	
1-1-95	16 at start	30		
4-1-95		5	25	
4-1-95	10 added	25		
5-1-95		13	12	This sum will give a rough
6-1-95		2	11	guide to your percentage
6-1-95	10 added	27		of alcohol. Expect a final
8-1-95		5	<u>22</u>	total of 120 to 170 for a
	Total sum		<u>70</u>	sweet mead.

Taste it. Recognise that harsh edge of fermentation. This takes about three months of subsequent storage to fall away significantly. Taste it again. Ignore the harsh background. Assess how sweet it is.

As the days go by the fermentation rate slows down and you need check only every few days. Keep the SG within the bounds set in the graph (fig 5.4F), narrowing to the final value desired. This is important because only in this way can a predictable sweet mead be assured.

A dry mead is allowed to run out of sugar, and thus never has the full alcohol quantity attainable. A sweet mead stops fermenting because the level of alcohol, reaching around 17%, either kills off the yeast or prevents further sugar conversion. But racking is necessary next. That is, to siphon the mead off the sediment.

Demijohns

A wine or mead maker often collects more big jars as he extends his involvement. These demijohns, from varying sources are not always exactly the same size. I have seen as much as 8oz (0.22 litre) difference between two supposedly 4.5L jars. Spillage and loss of the precious hooch can be avoided when siphoning if you are aware of this fact. With 5 litre versions around now this principle becomes quite essential. I mark each of my jars with a size difference. This with respect to one special reference demijohn. Chinagraph or other waxy crayon is ideal for marking jars and bottles.

Racking

A by-product of fermentation is a light muddy precipitate which settles at the bottom of the vessel. It usually swirls about readily with the slightest turbulence. It is wise to remove the

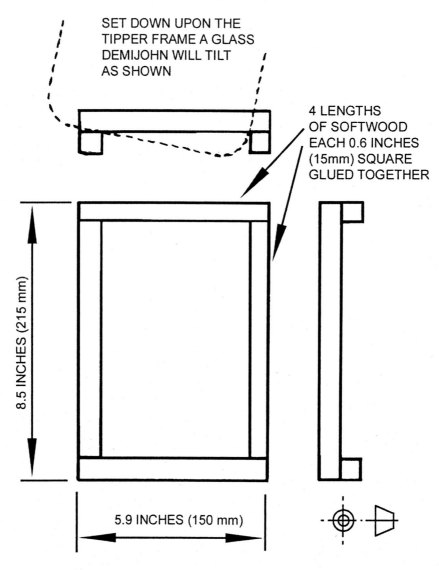

SET DOWN UPON THE TIPPER FRAME A GLASS DEMIJOHN WILL TILT AS SHOWN

4 LENGTHS OF SOFTWOOD EACH 0.6 INCHES (15mm) SQUARE GLUED TOGETHER

8.5 INCHES (215 mm)

5.9 INCHES (150 mm)

Fig 5.4C A simple tipper frame

worst of it shortly after fermentation as it can incur off-tastes if left. Yet more will settle out during the following months and need removing later.

Siphon the first six ounces or so of liquid into a jug and then transfer the flow into the receiving demijohn. In this way you avoid the risk of an overflow in the final moments, just when your attention is needed to watch for the last of the liquid without sucking up any dregs. I made a tipper frame (see fig 5.4C), an oblong frame of timber in which a jar won't set down flat upon the table. The last of the wine runs to one side and retains a bit of siphonable depth almost to the last. This delicate, last stage of the separation is helped if the level difference is reduced by raising the receiving jar, thereby slowing the flow, also if the jar is propped up slightly to one side so that more of the liquid can be taken.

The racking done, the new jar can be topped up easily from the jug. If any liquid is left over, it can be stored in a wine bottle to add to a later racking. I normally rack about three times during maturation, over about 5 to 10 months. This depends upon how much sediment is further precipitated.

*Fig 5.4D Mead: siphoning from the
sediment, slowing the flow*

When it has stood for several months and is deemed ready to bottle, the final racking is performed, but special regard should be given to sweet meads. The problem is that during two or more years of ageing, in the spring, when temperatures are rising again, a niggling refermentation usually begins to stir. (This never happens with dry meads.) But sugar is present. Pressure builds up. The cork is pushed out. That harsh taste returns and the object of maturation is frustrated. You can solve this quite satisfactorily if you go to the trouble to pasteurise, ie raise the liquid to a temperature which will kill any remaining yeast. Pasteurising and bottling are expediently done together.

What you need:

    Two, one gallon (4.5l) metal oil cans. Cut the tops off
    One thermometer to measure the range 40 to 100degC
    Seven wine bottles per gallon of mead. Corks. Corker
    Funnel to suit the bottles.

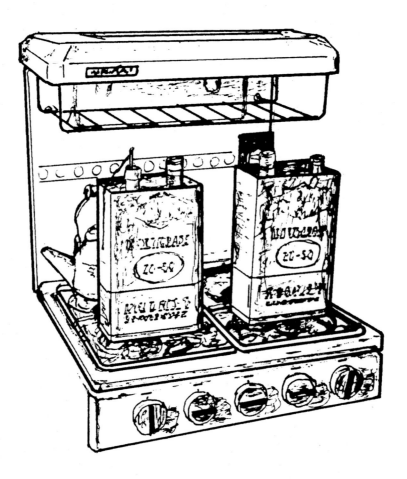

Fig 5.4E Mead: pasteurising prevents refermenting

Find loose-fit metal mesh or perforated zinc pieces to sit in the bottoms of the cans. This stops the bottles from banging and clunking. Distribute each gallon of mead equally into seven bottles, six of which will be their final housing. This should not quite fill them.

Stand two of the bottles in each of the two cans. Stand the two cans each on a gas or electric stove, side by side. See fig 5.4E. Add water to nearly fill the cans.

In a scheme to move each bottle one position to the left each few minutes as its temperature rises, the hottest will be the one on the extreme left. This one will need lifting out

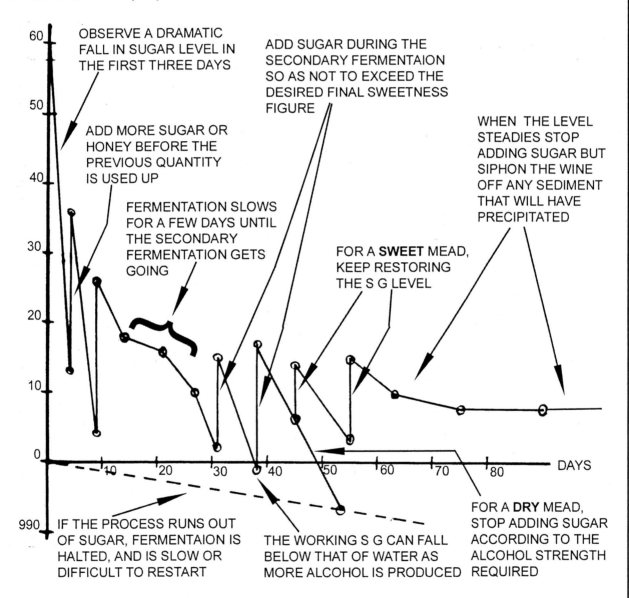

Fig 5.4F Mead: Monitoring the sugar levels: graph of SG against time

when its temperature has reached 75degC, and each of the others will need to be moved along, leaving the right position empty. This is filled by the next cold bottle.

As this progression is maintained, the heat under the left hand can is adjusted to keep the water in it at over 90degC. The water in the right hand can must be held at asignificantly lower temperature in order not to crack the newly inserted, cold bottles. A temperature of 65degC is suggested for this, and therefore a lower heat setting for the right hand side.

Before the mead is cold six bottles are topped up from the seventh before corking.

This process does not affect the qualities of the mead. If all other criteria are right, it will still win at the shows. I have used it many times, usually for three to five gallons at a time, and have had no refermentation troubles.

A dry mead could be ideal for drinking in two years; a sweet mead in four years.

Typical Fermentation Pattern

1. Observe a dramatic fall in sugar level in the first three days.
2. Measure the SG. at least each two days for the first week.
3. Add more sugar or honey before the previous quantity is used up.
4. The working SG. can fall below that of water as more alcohol is produced.
5. Fermentation normally gets under way within a few hours.
6. If the process runs out of sugar fermentation is halted, and is slow or difficult to restart.
7. Fermentation slows for a few days until the secondary fermentation gets going.
8. Don't add all the sugar at the start. It sometimes causes the fermentation to stick.
9. When the level steadies, stop adding sugar, but siphon the wine off any sediment that will have precipitated.
10. Add sugar during the secondary fermentation so as not to exceed the desired final sweetness figure.
11. For a sweet mead, keep restoring the SG. level.
12. For a dry mead, stop adding sugar according to the alcohol strength desired.

Solar Panels

By the time a beekeeper has been managing colonies for about three years, the need to salvage wax from old combs has become apparent. Six years and his stock of wax begins to accumulate. The small beekeeper settles to make a solar panel because the energy required is free and plentiful, he can manage it where he resides for best convenience, and he can make the size best suited to his needs. The construction is also well within the capacity of most handymen. There are other methods of rendering old comb but all are thirsty for fuelled energy, although the perennial advantage of these alternatives lies in their readiness all year round. The solar panel can only be used in the summer. Nevertheless, the solar panel ideally serves the purposes of the small beekeeper.

The solar panel can be constructed at home, and does lend itself to exploiting recycled or scavenged materials. One has only to see half a dozen spare time creations to realize the scope of resourcefulness and ideas. I have discovered that metal is quite unnecessary for the melting tray or for the receiving canister. They can be made of timber and they work just as well. The calculated omission of all unnecessary metalwork enables the panel to be made with carpentry tools. The worst solar panel that might have only one sheet of glass and no insulation will usually build up enough heat to melt beeswax. It might need the hottest day in July in southern England. But we can do a lot better than that with only a little thought and preparation. Most solar boxes can handle so much wax that they spend many useful sunny days

Fig 6.0A The larger the solar panel, the more arrangements of frames can be fitted in
It is a great advantage if it is big enough to accept a queen excluder

waiting for work. My two panels spend the winter months stowed indoors. Each has a tailored, plastic faced fabric cover for inclement weather. They keep dust off too during storage.

The Glaze

These days many well used panels are having their broken glass panes replaced by the modern, polycarbonate plastic double and triple glaze sheets. These are less expensive than glass and stand up well to high impacts and clumsy handling. The sizes needed for our panels, about one metre high by 0.75 metres wide can be obtained in large quantities from the offcuts produced in the outbuildings, roofing industry. The triple glaze is made up to 160mm thick, and this satisfies the greatest demand. The double glaze version, at 10mm thick, is just as suitable in my opinion.

The flutes are normally arranged up-and-down to give a degree of ventilation. This enables condensation to clear. One face is usually pre-treated to absorb ultra-violet radiation. This side is meant to face outwards. The 160mm triple glazed unit in my panel has had ten summers' bakings now and is unaffected by heat, wear or weather.

When in use, the inner face is held at a higher temperature and expands. This causes a slight tendency to bow, causing the top and bottom to rise slightly. I mention this to explain my advice to provide a pair of clips, or turnbuckles, each at top and bottom to hold the sheet flat.

The Tray

The traditional material for the inner tray is sheet metal. Tin plate, aluminium, stainless steel; all have been used. All are difficult to obtain, difficult to work, and expensive. Even if the metal sheet is free, you've still a taxing task in cutting and shaping it. The tray of the first of my two solar boxes is of stainless steel. It was made by a skilled sheet metal worker. But I, although with many years in light engineering, manufacturing electrical equipment, including three years as a toolmaker, would not have been capable of making it. If you must have a metal tray, it is worth remembering that the suppliers' of these manufactured panels will sell the metal trays as separate items, leaving you to manage only the carpentry. But few offered on sale are anywhere as big as one you can make.

Hardened customary thinking takes years to erode, even with the pressures of reason. In face of this I propose timber as a better alternative to metal. A wooden inner tray with a base made of external ply is perfectly suited for this purpose. It is easy to cut, and screw or glue together, and can be cleaned down with boiling water and a scraper. I've used one for ten years, and yearn for nothing better.

Significant advantage is to be gained if the inner tray of the solar panel is big enough to accept an 18 inches (45cm) square queen excluder, or whatever the size for your hive system. It means that you can melt the brace comb off the excluders on days that you've no wax to process. Don't waste your time scraping them clean. There's very little scraping needed once it's been well solared. A solar panel of this size will also accept crown and floor boards if need be. Furthermore, the bigger it is, the more combinations of frame arrangements can be accommodated. A good, hot, sunny day will melt all the wax out of combs stacked two deep. Remember this when determining your tray depth.

The Insulation

Many common materials may be considered to select for the insulation. Old carpets, underfelts, foamed plastics, fibreglass. Even layers of newspapers. All have been used. Avoid white, expanded polystyrene. It doesn't stand up to the high temperatures. Polyfoam (expanded polyurethane.) isn't much better. The best I've found is bonded underfelt.

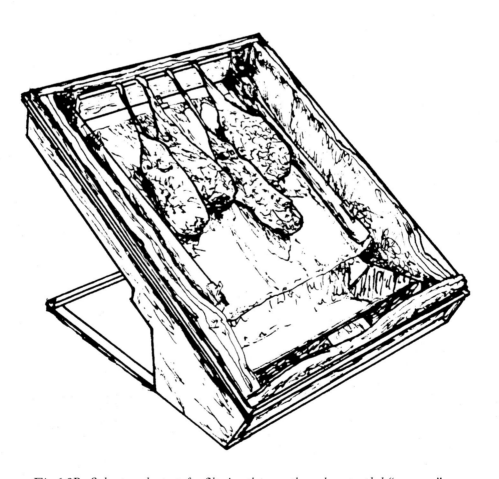

Fig 6.0B Solar panel set up for filtering the wax through suspended "sausages"

The Enclosing Box

The best sheet to make the outer box from is 4mm external grade plywood. It has no special problems in cutting, or screwing and gluing together. A coat of varnish (insist on an external grade for the outside faces) always enhances the natural grain appearance and gives even more protection from weather. The window type frame that holds the glazing sheet must

1) lift off easily
2) seal off air gaps to prevent heat from escaping
3) be rain proof

A common error in construction is to make the bottom well too small. It is a great convenience if the pot can be lifted out of the bottom well without first having to lift out the inner tray. To this end it pays well to make a scale drawing and plan the project well, perhaps looking at one or two panels in use and asking about their advantages and disadvantages, before committing oneself to cutting timber. If the collector pot is positioned so that the wax drips just one inch inside the back of the pot, and a good space is left in front of the pot, then it can be slid say two inches forward before lifting out.

The Collector Pot

A favourite, ready-made pot is the loaf tin. Cheap and readily available from kitchen suppliers, I soon found that even the biggest I ever found, a 2lb (0.9Kg) loaf size, albeit a rare size, was too small and sometimes ran the risk of overflowing. Releasing the block from the tin wasn't easy either

1)   My answer to this was to make a plywood pot, glued together well, and varnished. It can be made any shape or size, even to fit the full width of the well in which it is to sit.
2)   I lined this pot with Melinex®, a high temperature tolerant, transparent plastic film. This facilitates easy release of the wax when cold and lasts for at least two years, with reasonable care.

In cases where there is either no honey at all present, or lots of honey, release is easy. It is only when there is a little honey left in the old combs that there is any release difficulty at all. In this case some water helps to dissolve the honey and release the wax from the film.

The Filter Mesh

A coarse mesh is all that is needed. I doubt whether one inch square apertures would be too big. One of my filters is made of iron, expanded metal. It is not plated, and after ten years usage there is no trace of rust on it. When it gets caked up with waxy dirt I hold it over a bucket with a pair of pliers and run boiling water down it from the top. Thus softened it is the more readily loosened with a wire brush. A task for the garden, well away from the kitchen.

Keeping Rain Out

Following wet weather, a pool of water is sometimes found in the pot well; the lowest point. Unless the well is flooded the most expedient vector for removal is several layers of newspaper above and below the insulation in the well area. The water is readily soaked up and can easily be removed, and the panel then dried. This, of course until you discover and close the ingress route. Consider making drainage holes.

Usage

If you have more than half a dozen hives, then the pile of old combs that have been withdrawn in the spring and await a stint in the solar panel can take two or even four weeks to process, and the weather seems so unreliable that one feels that it is a race against the wax moth, though a suggestion for temporary protection is given in chapter 3.7. Once in block form though, the wax is immune from the attentions of this sinister devil.

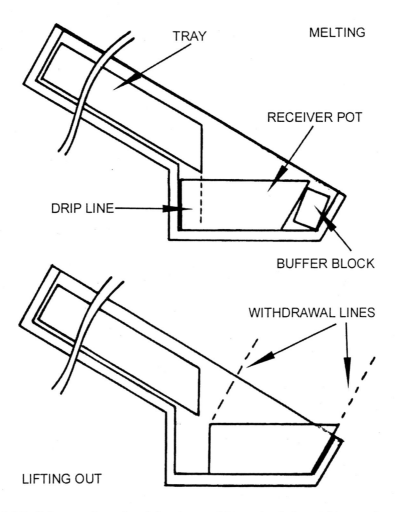

Fig 6.0C Solar panels, sectional drawing: making a plan before picking up the tools

Old combs can be fitted into the melting tray in best packing density, frame and all; two or even three deep if a hot day is expected. Only the metal ends and any drawing pins need be taken off beforehand. When pushed to handle more old comb, when the tray is full of frames, one can always cut an extra comb or two out of their frames and fit them into unused corners of the tray. The frames can be dealt with later. Nevertheless, patchy sessions of sunshine are often encountered which melt out only half the wax. This will be from the combs on top, and thus these nearly empty frames can be removed and replaced by full frames. This does at least derive the best of what sunny heat is available.

Strain and Wing Venation

Should a beekeeper have say ten hives and note down in his records his observations on trends and habits, both desirable and otherwise, he will soon realise that, averaged over the year, there are several differences between any two colonies. Indeed, the readiness with which the members of a colony will sting its owner during an inspection is most arresting and always comes top of a list. But there are several other traits both for and against which one should take due note of such as:

> propensity to swarm
> gumming up the hive with propolis
> overwintering qualities
> resistance to disease
> accuracy of comb building

There are many others. Long lists have been published (*Brother Adam, 1975*). Just pick on four or five that are important to you, allocate a reasonable loading figure to each, and use your recorded notes to give each hive a totted up score at the end of the season. These observations are the first, essential part of strain improvement: identifying the queen from which to propagate. Queen rearing is the other part.

Having allocated and compared the complex hive scoring figures, you will note the great differences between the values of the strains. The long established purpose is to requeen each of the other nine hives through a queen rearing, or queen selection, exercise, centred around that hive giving the best composite marks. A general improvement can be expected.

The statutory first placing of aggression on these lists of undesirables has been increasingly challenged in recent years. This will continue.

The new ideal is genetic stability. In simple terms, purity of strain. That strain which is adapted to get the best of the local flora, upon which it depends, that upon which no honeybee from elsewhere in the country, or in the world, is suited. This quality can be assessed quite effectively in fact, by any beekeeper who likes to take the trouble to make the measurements. Discriminating keepers are using these techniques to assess each colony or each queen for selection and breeding. This is because once one's queens are little affected by a heredity of

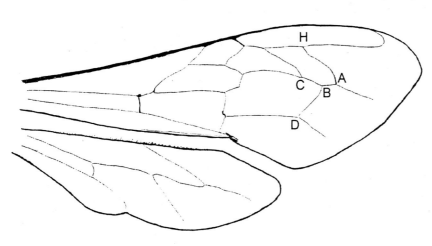

Fig 6.1A Wing venation

incessant and haphazard hybridisation, then the effect of breeding by selection becomes more effective and lasts longer.

Assessment of purity of strain can be achieved through close measurements of wing venation and other bee parts. This is by studying morphology. Growing importance is being given to this back room analysis in consolidating desirable qualities in a colony of honeybees. Furthermore, such measurements are quite within the capabilities of today's do-it-yourselfer without overstraining his resources. The most sophisticated equipment needed is a slide projector; more likely to be found in the average household perhaps than a microscope.

Over the last 100 years there have been spurious and long lasting ripples of disturbance, county-wide, in the British strain of honeybees, caused by continued importation of foreign queens. With the promise of short term gains, which have rarely, if ever, been substantiated, the introduction of such queens ushers in genes adapted for other climates and conditions which are then spread by cross breeding with neighbouring bee colonies and disrupt the subtle, long-term, natural adjustment to the local flora and climate.

Selection, based on genetic assessments, can not only buffer this wide spreading perturbation, but this study of wing venation provides evidence of restoration via the effectiveness of selection in order to achieve improvements in all the other criteria mentioned above.

Basics

A bee's wings are laced with a net of fine veins. The net for a front and rear pair of wings is illustrated in fig 6.1A, and a small area of the fore wing expanded (fig 6.1D) in order to show what we are looking for.

The position of junction B varies slightly from one bee to another. In some samples it is nearer to junction A than in others. We measure this in terms of a ratio, BC divided by AB. This gives a figure that varies between 1.3 and at least 2.5. It is called the CUBITAL INDEX.

Similarly the position of junction D varies with respect to junction H. We measure the horizontal (fig 6.1E) variations with respect to junction H and express them in degrees, normally between +8 and -8. + is towards the wing tip. This is called the DISCOIDAL SHIFT.

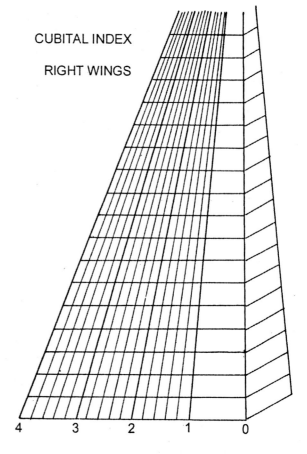

CUBITAL INDEX

RIGHT WINGS

Fig 6.1B Graticule. Measuring template for Cubital Index. Not to scale (Dews & Milner, 1991)

One needs a sample of at least 30 wings from the colony under examination. If the wings are cut from worker bees that are already taken for disease tests, then none are unnecessarily sacrificed. Use wings only from one side, this simplifies the measuring procedures and avoids confusion of samples.

The Mounting Medium

To prepare for the measurements, the thirty wings are mounted, sandwiched in two glass, 35mm, projector, slide mounts; fifteen per mount. Glass slide-mounts can be bought, 20 to a box, from most photo dealers. Various methods of holding the wings in place on the slides have been suggested. I found a roll of double sided sticky tape; a transparent film stickied on both sides, interleaved with waxy paper worked best. Three cut strips, each 1.5 x 22 mm will mount 15 to 18 wings on a slide.

A template, a card, which is no more than a graticule printed onto thick paper which comes with a book, *Dews & Milner (1991)*, facilitates accurate measurements. This card is held against a wall (fig 6.1H) and the wing images are projected onto it. Each image venation is aligned in turn and the cubital index can be simply read off. The card is then turned over and a different template similarly provides for the discoidal shift figures. Thus about thirty pairs of values can be recorded in only a few minutes use of the projector. A discrete screen is unnecessary and a wall is far more suitable.

Two readings, two figures, are obtained for each wing. The next step is to plot each pair of readings on to a prepared graph. This will give thirty spots, to form a cluster that we call a SCATTERGRAM (fig 6.1G).

Now we can start deriving some answers. A tight and compact bunch of dots indicates a good, stable strain. The position of the centre of the cluster also yields essential information. A natural British strain will show a cluster towards the lower left hand corner. Scattergrams from colonies evolved in different parts of

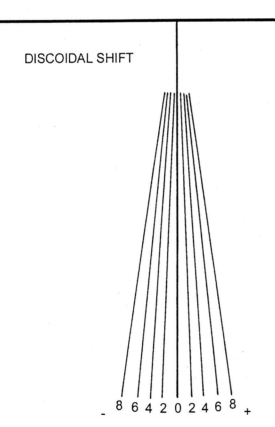

Fig 6.1C 'T' Graticule. Measuring template for Discoidal Shift. Not to scale (Dews & Milner, 1991)

Europe are to be found centred in very different points on the graph. Typical figures:

Apis mellifera	A mellifera British	A ligustiga Italian	A carniola Balkan
Cubital index	1.7	2.3	2.7
Discoidal shift	Negative	Positive	Positive

The scattergrams from any one hive are closely repeatable, even from year to year, and do show up the differences between any two colonies. If the spots you plot are all over the page, or even beyond, then your bees, like all of mine when I made my tests, are forlorn mongrels. I live in S.W.London. The bees still accumulate honey and wax, but their traits are not very predictable. Were the bees truly indigenous, the traits from hive to hive should be identical. They are not. Today's beekeepers are increasingly recognising strain as more important than any of the other criteria.

This is but a brief outline of the studies, courses and books created, collected, organised and available from the Bee Improvement and Bee Breeders' Association (BIBBA), the following and influence of which is steadily gathering momentum.

I keep about ten hives. Any colony that I have kept going for two years or more is either good tempered or very good indeed. I rarely need smoke or gloves. This is because a declining or missing queen is always replaced from one of my other hives, one with a desirable track record, one of those with the best aggregate of tolerance to hive inspections. In recent years this has set a generally workable temperament in the bees enabling me to set up tests and to make suitable observations without smoke or gloves.

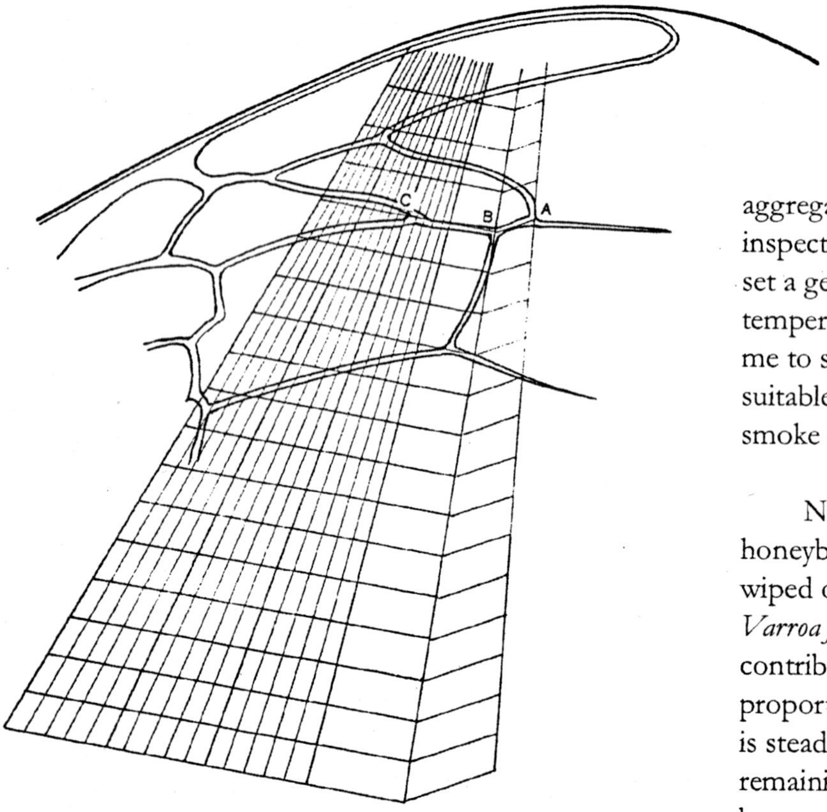

Now that all the wild (unkept) honeybees are being inexorably wiped out by the parasite spider *Varroa jacobsonii*, then the genetic contribution of this natural proportion of the bee community is steadily disappearing. The remaining apian population of kept bees are our only remaining opportunity to exercise some control over stability.

Fig 6.1D Cubital index: Interlace diagram. Align the ladder to match points A and B. Read off the Cubital Index at point C.

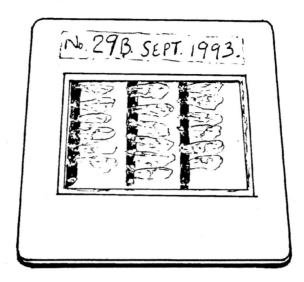

Fig 6.1F Wings mounted. Up to 18 wings can be set in a slide mount.

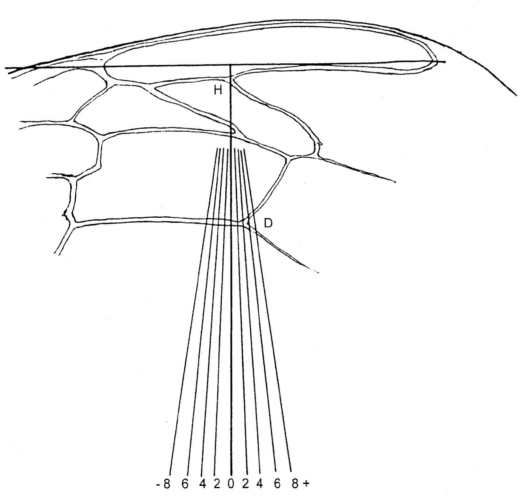

-8 6 4 2 0 2 4 6 8 +

Fig 6.1E Discoidal Shift: Interlace diagram. Align the top line along the long radial cell with the junction set on point H. The horizontal line must pass through the extreme points of the radial cell for the angle at D to be accurate. Read the Discoid Shift at point D.

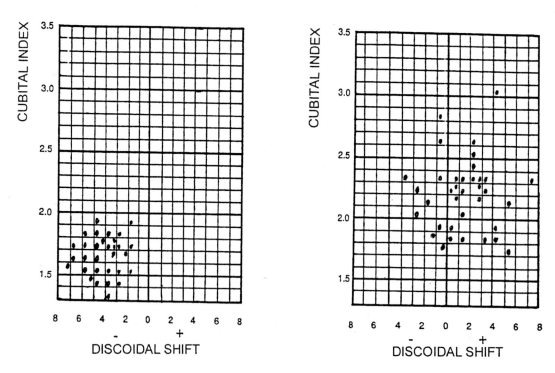

Fig 6.1G Scattergrams. (Left) An example for the indigenous black, British Isles honeybee. (Dews & Milner, 1991). (Right) All my London bees produce scattergrams like this.

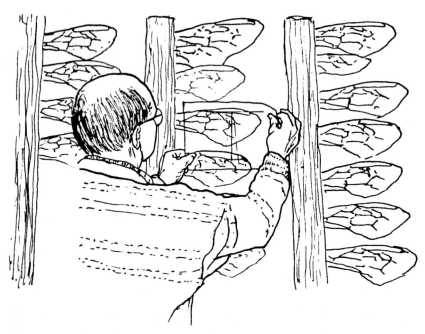

Fig 6.1H No need for a screen. Focus the projector on a wall. Position the printed card. Simply read off the figures.

References

2.8   Hamer, John; April 1993, Beecraft: "Foundation Press"

3.0   Jeff Davies; January 1996, Letter in Beecraft: "Beekeeping Hints and Tips"

3.8   Hooper, Ted; 1976, Blandford Press: "Guide to Bees and Honey"

3.9   Martin, Dr S. 1998, *Varroa jacobsoni*: monitoring and forecasting mite populations within honeybee colonies in Britain.

4.4   Hamer, John; April 1994, Beecraft: "Cappings Separator".

5.0   Coggeshall and Morse; 1984, 1995, Wicwas Press, Cheshire, CT, USA: "Beeswax"

5.1   Padmore, F A;   National Honey Show Publication: "Wax for Show"

5.2   Hodges, D; 1958, IBRA: "The Pollen Loads of the Honeybee"

5.2   N.B.S. An alternative method of collecting and staining pollen (This data is now embodied into the second edition of White 1989). N.B.S., Ipswich

5.2   White, J H.; 1989, From N.B.S., Ipswich: "Pollen, its Collection and Preparation for the Microscope"

5.2   Cook V A and Wilkinson P D; Oct 1986, British Bee Journal: "Pollen Feeding Boosts Brood in Colonies"

5.2   Sawyer Rex; 1981, University College Cardiff Press: "Pollen Identification for Beekeepers"

5.4   Furness C; 1972, Northern Bee Books: "Honey Wines and Beers"

6.0   Chapman N J; March/April 1991, Beecraft: "The 1990 Solar Panel"

6.1   Dews J E and Milner E; 1991, BIBBA: "Breeding Better Bees"

6.1   Brother Adam; 1975, British Bee Publications: "Beekeeping at Buckfast Abbey"

EXAMINATION.			WORKERS.			COMBS.			QUEEN.			DRONES.		HIVE & STORES.				HEALTH & NOTES.
Date.	Main task.	Smoke.	Aggr-ession.	Calm ness.	Follo wing.	Pollen stores.	Brood nest shape.	Frames of brood.	Seen. Marks.	Worker ELCM	Queen cells.	Amount	ELCM	Boxes.		Lbs.		
														Brood.	Supers	Sugar fed.	Honey. stores.	

HIVE RECORD.   YEAR.   HIVE.

20											
20											
20											
Year.	Fecundity. Max no of fr. of brood.	Super-cedure. Y/N	Queen age. Month/year & origin	Attempts to swarm.	Distorted combs. No of combs.	Brood combs withdrawn.	Agression. 0 to 100 100is best.	Calmness. 0 to 100 100is best.	Following. 0 to 100 100is best.	Honey yield. lbs.
20											

EXAMINATION.			WORKERS.			COMBS.			QUEEN.			DRONES.		HIVE & STORES.				HEALTH & NOTES.
Date.	Main task.	Smoke.	Aggr-ession.	Calm ness.	Follo wing.	Pollen stores.	Brood nest shape.	Frames of brood.	Seen. Marks.	Worker ELCM	Queen cells.	Amount	ELCM	Boxes.		Lbs.		
														Brood.	Supers	Sugar fed.	Honey. stores	